PRACTICAL PIG PRODUCTION

DEDICATION

To Shirley,
also Peter, Janet and Gillian,
but not forgetting
Butch, Betsy and Davey.

PRACTICAL PIG PRODUCTION

KEITH THORNTON

B Sc (Agriculture)

FARMING PRESS LIMITED
WHARFEDALE ROAD, IPSWICH, SUFFOLK

First published 1973
Second (revised) edition 1978
Third edition 1981
Reprinted 1984
ISBN 0 85236 115 7

This book is set in 10pt on 11pt Times and is printed in Great Britain by Essex Telegraph Press Ltd, Colchester.

ACKNOWLEDGEMENTS

FIRST EDITION

FIRST OF ALL, my acknowledgements to the Reverend Peter Buckler who originally encouraged me in my work with pigs, and to Richard Weaver who sustained this interest at a later time. I am also grateful to the Royal Agricultural Society of England and to the Managers' Committee of the Pig Demonstration Area at the Nationsl Agricultural Centre who have allowed me to refer freely to my work at the NAC. I am also indebted to members of the Meat and Livestock Commission, particularly those pig specialists with whom I worked closely over a number of years, and to Mike Strang of the ADAS Liaison Unit at NAC and to other ADAS staff. Whilst at Stoneleigh I also worked closely with David Allot and John Young at the Farm Buildings Centre and much of this work is summarised in the Housing Sections of this book.

I would also like to pay tribute to the work carried out by Dr David Sainsbury at Cambridge and also to David Soutar and Seaton Baxter and their staff at the Scottish Farm Buildings Investigation Unit. I have also drawn heavily from the book, *Pig Production*, which is the Proceedings of the 18th Easter School in Agricultural Science, University of Nottingham, edited by Dr D. J. A. Cole.

I would like to thank Dr Brian Cooke, of Crosfields Farm Foods Ltd, for his valuable comments on my chapter on Feeding, and also my other colleagues and members of staff at Clifton who progressed the book in a variety of ways. In the chapter on Health I am grateful for help from Charles Roberts, of Wickham Laboratories, and also from Alan Baldry, of the ADAS Unit at Stoneleigh, who read through this chapter and made some helpful comments and suggestions.

Many of the photographs were supplied by *Pig Farming*, whose staff reporter, Martin Looker [now editor], took many of them himself and located others in their library. Geoffrey Wickens, of Pig Breeders Supply Company, supplied photographs No. 24 and 25, and I would also like to thank the Curtis family for their help and for supplying photographs Nos. 1, 7, 12 and 32 which were taken on Northern Pig Development Co. farms in the East Riding. Photograph No. 4 was supplied by Farm Buildings Centre. All the housing diagrams and most of the illustrations were prepared and drawn by Nick Noton, Chartered Surveyor and Farm Buildings Consultant of Morcott, Uppingham. I would also like to thank MLC for permission to use diagrams No. 36 and 37, and the Electricity Council for diagram 9 from their Farmelectric Handbook No. 10—Controlled Environment.

I have also referred to a large amount of published information including books, periodicals, magazines and lecture notes which have come my way over the past few years. In most cases the sources have been acknowledged but occasionally this has not been possible. A selection of these references appears at the end of the book for further reading.

Bernard Hogley, editor of *Pig Farming* [now retired], encouraged me to write and I must thank Philip Wood, of Farming Press Books, for his guidance and forbearance whilst the book has been in production. I should also like to thank Mrs Woodley, Mrs Rose, Mrs Wood and Mrs Preston for their help in the typing, production and correction of this book.

Above all, my thanks to the many thousands of farmers who visited Stoneleigh over the past few years and for their questions, discussion and debate which made this book possible.

KEITH THORNTON

ACKNOWLEDGEMENTS

SECOND EDITION

I WOULD like to thank MLC Pig Improvement Services and Economics Information Services for their help with the revision and updating of the tables and figures in the book, particularly in the first three chapters. The Managers Committee of the NAC Demonstration Area kindly provided the figures to bring the NAC Pig Unit results up to date.

Nick Noton again allowed me to use the drawings and diagrams on housing, and figures 6, 7, 8, 9, 13, 14 and 26 were redrawn by Geoff Fielding of Swiftpine (Agricultural Consultants). I am particularly grateful for the assistance from John Barnett in working out the tables and calculating the figures for the 250-sow unit in Chapter 11—a very tricky area.

Finally, to my wife Shirley and daughter Gillian who coped with the mass of revised figures, corrections and re-typing, all under considerable pressure from the author.

January, 1978   KEITH THORNTON

ACKNOWLEDGEMENTS

THIRD EDITION

REVISIONS for the Third Edition have been made whilst I am working in the USA, and I am grateful to the MLC for the use of their publications, especially the *MLC Commercial Pig Production Yearbook 1980*. This is an up-to-date and excellent review of the economics and of the facts and figures of pig production as they affect the producer.

David Allott, in Reading, was also extremely helpful at the end of a number of searching transatlantic telephone calls to complete various tables. My daughter Janet, on vacation in USA from Sydney, Australia, helped with the revisions and typing. Finally, I must thank my colleagues and staff at PIC for their time, trouble and help in making this revision possible.

Wisconsin
June, 1981   KEITH THORNTON

CONTENTS

ILLUSTRATIONS

11

DIAGRAMS

12

FOREWORD

by SIR HENRY PLUMB

President, The National Farmers' Union

WHEN KEITH THORNTON asked me to write the foreword for the first edition of *Practical Pig Production* in 1973, the conditions in the pig industry and its outlook for the future were vastly different from what they are now. We had then just entered the Common Market and had five years of transition ahead of us, by which time we expected to be on equal footing with pig producers in other parts of the Community. We could not have foreseen the fall in value of sterling which led to the massively subsidised imports of pigmeat that have undermined our market so disastrously.

Nevertheless, these things have happened and, as a result, our pig breeding herd has dropped from one million in 1973 to around 800,000 at the end of 1977. The total consumption of pigmeat in the UK has fallen from 918,000 tonnes in 1973 to an estimated 838,000 tonnes in 1977. Despite this fall, the UK share of the total pigmeat market rose from 64 per cent to nearly 68 per cent, but this was only achieved at the expense of producer profitability in 1974 and again in 1976/77.

It is clear that pigmeat consumption, in common with other meats, has been severely hit by the effect of the country's economic ills of the last few years. However, the advent of North Sea oil means that the financial climate is changing and with it, hopefully, we shall see an improvement in demand for meat and meat products. If the British pigmeat producer is to be able to gain a greater share of this increased demand, it is essential that the monetary compensatory amounts on imported pigmeat are reduced. A cut in the Green Pound would help, but it is imperative that the method of calculating the mca's for pigmeat must be revised as well. If these two aspects are achieved, I believe that the pig industry can look forward with confidence to a continuing major role in the pattern of farming and in the economy of the country.

However, changes are taking place rapidly in the structure of pig farming and it will therefore be essential for pig producers to practise the highest standard of husbandry and business management if they wish to succeed. In this respect they will find Mr Thornton's book invaluable.

January, 1978   HENRY PLUMB

PREFACE

TO THE FIRST EDITION

THIS IS a book about practical pig farming. I have taken a personal view of this friendly and valuable animal and have put these views down in reasonably simple terms. Almost everyone has some contact with keeping pigs, much of this going back to the time when the cottager's sty was a traditional and essential part of the country dweller's way of life. In exchange for household scraps and a few vegetables the pig provided the farmer with both meat and company throughout the year and was a vital part of his domestic economy. In fact, a few pigs still lurk in the allotments outside Leamington Spa and many other towns throughout the country! Part of the pig's appeal and popularity is explained when we consider the difficulty of keeping a dairy cow under similar circumstances.

But times have changed. Over the past nine years I was privileged to be the manager of the NAC Pig Demonstration Unit and in a special position to both observe and take part in the technical changes that occurred in the pig industry during this time. Much of the content of this book is based upon these experiences, but I have also drawn from many other sources.

Throughout this period Stoneleigh became a base not only for practical demonstrations, but also a forum for discussion and for the exchange of ideas and points of view. In this way the changes that were taking place in the pig industry were reflected in changes in the NAC pig unit, in particular the trend towards specialisation and more intensive methods of production with an emphasis on management, pig performance and profitability. With these points in mind, this book is written for a large section of the people involved in the pig industry, especially the progressive pig farmer. The contents should also appeal to students at agricultural colleges and universities who are following a general course but who may need a specialist view of pig farming. Throughout the book, I have attempted to review the scientific facts that have emerged in recent years and have tried to present them in an accurate and practical way. Not everyone will agree with my viewpoints and presentation, but fortunately there is plenty of room for disagreement. Many of the details such as costs, prices and returns will inevitably change but the basic principles remain ths same.

Probably this is the first book on pigs that does not include a list and description of the various breeds of pigs. I have concentrated on the crossbred as much as our traditional pig production is still based on this type of animal. More recently we have seen the introduction of the crossbred or hybrid gilt. It must, however, be remembered that the hybrid pig will only be as good as its purebred parents so that it is vital that the improvement of our pure breeds is continued.

The selection of type of housing for our pigs is almost as wide as ever, with strong regional preferences. I have narrowed this selection down to one or two choices and this I think reflects the standardisation and specialisation that is taking place in pig housing.

In the chapter on feeding I have reviewed much of the research work that has taken place and reached some conclusions which I know work in practice. The management and husbandry sections are also based on practical experience of intensive pig farming. I firmly advise a preventive approach to pig health and have resisted the temptation to list all known pig diseases. Instead I have outlined some of the main principles of a plan for pig health based on preventive medicine.

In recording and management control I have highlighted the main factors affecting profitability and linked these to a business-like approach. This is now an essential part of profitable pig farming.

Somerset, KEITH THORNTON
July, 1973

PREFACE

TO THE SECOND EDITION

ALTHOUGH it is less than five years since the first edition was published, events have moved quickly in pig production. Against an increasingly difficult political and economic background, technical efficiency has further improved.

Emphasis is now on earlier weaning around three weeks of age and fewer, larger, and more specialist pig farms.

However, the basic principles of production have remained the same, but it is now even more essential to balance and co-ordinate the whole range of factors, especially breeding, feeding, housing, health and management.

Somerset, KEITH THORNTON
January, 1978

PREFACE

TO THE THIRD EDITION

THE THREE years since this book was last revised have not been very profitable for the UK pig producer. For most of the time I have been working in the Mid-West region of the USA, and have been able to follow through my PIC colleagues and *Pig Farming* magazine the problems and fortunes of the UK industry.

At the same time the USA hog industry has gone through the most difficult period for over 20 years, with the familiar cyclical pattern of low market prices and inflationary costs. Under these circumstances the answer here is towards fewer larger units, more specialisation and attention to the critical areas of breeding and management.

The US producer still looks toward Europe, and the UK in particular, for information and example in the technology of the intensive hog production. The British pig producer, through a difficult period, has shown over the past few years that he is still the best in the business.

Spring Green   KEITH THORNTON
Wisconsin, USA
June, 1981.

Chapter 1

STRUCTURE OF THE PIG INDUSTRY

THE PIG has always played an important part in UK meat production, providing a wide variety of meats including pork, bacon and ham, liver and kidneys, and other delicacies such as pig trotters. Add to these the other important products like pig skin and bristle and we can begin to appreciate the old saying about the pig, 'nothing wasted apart from its squeal'. The high quality manure has always been valuable in the farming industry, especially when the pig unit is integrated with arable systems, and for all these reasons the pig has been an important source of farm income and profit.

When we look at livestock production from UK farms we can see that pigs make a major contribution to farm output. At the farm gate pig production accounted for approximately 80 per cent of total livestock output and 7 per cent of the total value of agricultural output.

TABLE 1. Output of Livestock and Livestock Products from UK Farms
(£ million)

Type of product	74/75	75/76	June/May 76/77	77/78	78/79	79/80
Milk and milk products	928	1,187	1,340	1,620	1,761	1,928
Fat cattle and calves	745	960	1,046	1,258	1,423	1,492
Fat pigs	482	520	596	689	745	783
Eggs	281	296	366	400	462	488
Poultry	261	294	361	444	488	513
Fat sheep and lambs	164	206	260	300	319	382
Wool clip	17	20	23	33	35	35

Source: Annual Review of Agriculture 1981.

This may not be immediately apparent as we travel the countryside because over the past few years the pig industry has turned increasingly towards intensive methods of pig-keeping. This means that in general pigs have moved indoors and the trend continues, although there remains a hard core of outdoor pig production units.

18

There are a number of reasons for this trend, centred mainly around land and labour and the interaction between these two production factors. With a rapid increase in the price of land, modern farming methods must produce a better margin per hectare than could be obtained from extensive outdoor pig-keeping. This has been especially true on heavier land, which in any case was never very suitable for large-scale outdoor pig production.

Labour is unwilling to service these outdoor units under unfavourable conditions with the hazards of wind and weather creating sticky going for both man and animal. There is a general feeling, too, that management can be more easily controlled when the herd is housed indoors, and this is particularly important in the large herd. On light land and in low rainfall areas outdoor pig production will of course continue, and in these favourable areas there is generally a lower cost structure which is still yielding a useful profit.

There has been a recent revival of interest in outdoor production because of the increasing energy costs of intensive systems. A number of producers in the Oxford/Berkshire area have blended the best of the traditional outdoor methods with newer concepts such as weaning at 3 weeks of age.

TABLE 2. Pig Numbers in the UK: June
('000 head)

	1960	1968	1972	1975	1977	1978	1979	1980
Sows for breeding	725	887	960	814	820	841	847	833
Boars for service	40	44	45	40	41	42	43	42
Other pigs	4,958	5,956	7,613	6,592	6,738	6,824	6,954	6,757
Total pigs	5,723	6,887	8,608	7,449	7,599	7,707	7,844	7,632

Table 2 shows that the number of pigs increased rapidly from 1960 to 1972. In June 1960 there were 5·7 million pigs in the UK; by June 1972 this figure had risen to 8·6 million, an increase of 51 per cent. Since 1974 the number of pigs in the national herd has remained below 8·0 million, and due to a number of events, including the cyclical nature of pig production and the political and financial implications of transition to EEC membership, the national herd has fallen to its lowest level since 1965.

Table 3 shows the changes in the structure of the industry which have taken place in England and Wales since 1970. This analysis is based on the number of sows and gilts in herds of various sizes and illustrates quite clearly the rapidly increasing proportion of sows that are now being kept in the larger breeding herds. There has also been a remarkable reduction in the number of holdings with breeding stock, falling rapidly from 81,000 in 1960 to 40,800 in 1977. This indicates that about half of the producers with breeding stock in England and Wales in 1960 have since gone out of production, which is a dramatic change, and the trend continues.

The total number of sows and gilts in England and Wales has risen from 566,000 in 1960 to 815,000 at the end of 1980. With the reduction in the number of producers, the average breeding herd size has increased from 6·9 to 34·0 in 1980, with just over 24,000 holdings now with pigs.

TABLE 3. Percentages of sows and gilts in breeding herds of various sizes, England and Wales

Size of herd (sows and gilts)	1970	1974	1977
1	0·7	0·5	0·4
2–4	4·4	2·5	1·8
5–9	7·8	4·5	3·4
10–14	7·7	4·8	3·5
15–19	6·3	4·1	2·9
20–29	10·8	7·5	5·9
30–49	15·8	12·7	10·6
50–99	22·5	23·9	22·7
100–199	15·1	20·7	23·1
200–499	6·8	13·5	17·9
500 and over	2·1	5·3	7·8
	100	100	100

Source: MLC.

One significant factor is the increasing number of large herds, and quite clearly a large proportion of our pigmeat will be produced from relatively few farms. Within the next two or three years it seem likely that fewer than 10,000 farmers will produce over 80 per cent of the pigmeat in the UK.

Table 4 shows the situation in England and Wales for total pig numbers. In 1972 pigs were kept on 23 per cent of all agricultural holdings; by 1976 this proportion had fallen to below 16 per cent and by 1980 to just above 14 per cent.

Average herd size—breeding and feeding pigs—in 1976 was 206 pigs compared with 135 pigs in 1972. An interesting comparison can be made with leading EEC countries which shows UK with the largest average herd size, followed by Netherlands with 127 and Denmark with 84.

Table 5 shows the changes that have taken place in pig numbers on a regional basis. Also shown are changes that have occurred in average herd size since 1970 in these regions.

There has been a tendency for pig production to move away from the South West, Wales and the South East areas (in which cereal prices have often been high) to grain-growing areas in the east of the country.

The most rapid expansion has taken place in the Holderness and Humberside areas of Yorkshire and there are a number of reasons for this. As a major grain-producing area, feedingstuffs were available at very competitive rates, and the large sea port at Hull handles a great deal of imported timber, now widely used in the construction of new-style pig housing. With these raw materials at hand and a few pioneering

TABLE 4. The Proportion of Pigs in Herds of Various Sizes, England and Wales: June

Size of herd	1972	1973	1974	1975	1976
Under 10	0·6	0·5	0·5	0·5	0·4
10–29	3·0	2·4	2·1	1·8	1·5
30–49	3·2	2·7	2·2	1·9	1·8
50–99	7·8	6·7	5·8	4·9	4·4
100–199	12·1	11·2	10·3	8·9	8·1
200–499	25·8	24·3	22·4	} 43·4	} 42·1
500–999	21·3	21·7	22·1		
1,000–1,999	14·9	16·6	18·2	} 33·5	} 35·4
2,000–4,999	9·5	10·7	11·8		
5,000 and over	1·8	3·2	4·6	5·1	6·3
No. of pigs	6,910,018	7,297,070	7,088,276	6,337,197	6,661,781
No. of holdings with pigs	51,115	46,575	40,788	33,291	32,337
Average herd size	135·2	156·7	173·8	190·4	206·0
Total holdings	220,216	212,761	211,435	206,172	204,416
Per cent of holdings with pigs	23·2	21·9	19·3	16·2	15·8

Source: MAFF.

farmers, the breeding herd size in that area has increased by 30 per cent to 35 per cent, and it has become one of the leading areas for large-scale intensive pig production in the UK. Use of slatted floor systems has caused problems with slurry disposal, but lagoons have been used with some success, and after a period of storage the slurry has been spread on arable land.

TABLE 5. Regional Changes in Average Breeding Herd Size, No. of Holdings and Average Herd Size: June
('000 head)

Area	1970			1974			1977		
	SG	H	AHS	SG	H	AHS	SG	H	AHS
Eastern	232	8·5	27·3	252	6·5	38·8	248	4·9	50·6
South East	106	3·3	31·8	106	2·4	44·1	95	1·8	51·8
Midlands	107	7·3	14·8	104	4·9	21·3	92	3·5	26·5
South West	130	10·1	12·8	107	6·2	17·2	94	4·5	20·7
Northern	153	9·4	16·2	163	6·6	24·7	158	4·8	32·7
England	728	38·6	18·8	732	26·6	27·5	687	19·6	35·0
Wales	36	6·1	5·9	25	3·7	6·8	19	2·6	7·2
Scotland	71	3·6	19·5	62	2·2	28·9	56	1·3	42·0
Northern Ireland	118	17·5	6·7	70	10·8	6·5	66	8·1	8·2
United Kingdom	953	65·9	14·5	889	43·3	20·6	828	31·6	26·2

SG = No. of sows and gilts; H = No. of holdings; AHS = Average herd size.
Source: MLC.

This is the likely pattern for pig production, with large-scale intensive units even in the traditional arable areas. There is some indication that with increasing specialisation pig production could be divorced from the local supply of raw materials such as grain and straw. With continuous research into effluent disposal there may be a wider distribution of the pig population, with intensive units spread throughout the country. However, energy and environmental factors remain a key problem in the siting and operation of intensive pig units.

One final point that seems to be emerging from surveys of the national pig herd is the increasing number of self-contained breeding and feeding units. This factor and the increasing herd size with fewer units are probably the most important of the changes taking place within the structure of the UK pig herd at the present time, and the trend is continuing through the early part of the '80s.

Chapter 2

THE MARKET OUTLOOK

MARKETING OF pigmeat—which is normally a rather contentious subject—has been largely influenced by the political implications of full United Kingdom entry into the EEC. We are now part of a large population of pig producers, numbering around the two million mark, and in these circumstances any forecast may turn out to be pure speculation.

There is some firm ground to work from when we look at demand for meat products within the UK over the past few years. It is safe to predict that as the standard of living rises, however slowly, there will be an increase in the demand for meat products.

TABLE 6. **Estimated Consumption of Meat per Capita UK**[1]
(kg per head per annum)

	1938	1948	1972	1976	1977	1978	1979
Pork	4·8	8·7	12·3	10·4	11·5	12·0	12·3
Bacon and ham	12·7	11·4	11·2	8·6	9·0	9·2	9·2
Beef and veal[2]	24·9	23·4	21·0	21·0	22·9	22·5	21·5
Mutton and lamb	16·0	10·2	9·2	7·7	7·0	7·0	7·3
Poultry	2·3	4·3	12·0	11·6	12·1	12·9	13·3
Offal and canned meat	5·4	8·8	7·2	7·4	7·2	7·4	7·4

[1]These figures represent home production, plus imports, less exports, waste, and non-food uses, and adjusted for stocks. This total is divided by mid-year population to arrive at kg/head per annum figure.

[2]Includes bone-in beef and imported boneless beef converted to bone-in equivalent.

Based on MAFF data.

The trends in this table are quite clear, although these must be interpreted fairly carefully. There has been a large increase in the consumption of poultry meat and an almost similar increase in the demand for pork. The peak demand was reached in 1972 for both products, since when consumption of pork has declined along with a slight reduction in the consumption of poultry meat. Bacon and ham purchases have also dropped from previous levels, with a clear hint of

23

further decreases in the spending on these two products. Beef and veal have shown a steady decline in the housewife's shopping basket and the demand for mutton and lamb has shown the same pattern.

The slight increase in demand for offal and canned meats can be accounted for by a greater interest in delicatessen and cooked meat products that are now available.

Overall, this situation shows the decline from about 1972 in total demand for all meat products at a time when the housewife has had relatively less to spend on food out of the weekly housekeeping allowance.

However, demand for food and meat products has become very difficult to forecast in the past few years. This is because of incomes policy and wage restraints at national level, which have led to declining real incomes in the mid-1970s.

Various political factors have influenced the spending power of the consumer, but long-term forecasts indicate that there appears to be a possibility that the UK will return to an annual growth of real disposable income of approximately 2 to 3 per cent in the mid 1980s. Meanwhile the current depressed state of the economy and high unemployment force consumers to be extremely selective and cautious in their purchase of meat and meat products.

One other major factor that should be taken into consideration is the UK population statistics. A peak level of almost 56 million people was reached in 1976 and there is a forecast of a slight reduction between 1976 and 1979. There are, however, indications of a recovery in numbers between 1971 and 1981, with a return to the peak figure of 1976.

Looking at the pigmeat market against this background, pork is well placed to continue to obtain an increasing share of the total meat market. Consumption rose by about 20 per cent between 1955 and 1975, but forecasts indicate that demand will increase at a much lower figure over the next few years—perhaps by 10 to 12 per cent. The bulk of pork is of course home produced, and rapid access to our domestic markets for fresh meat is a big advantage for the UK producer. Beef and veal consumption are forecast to show a marked decline in the next few years, so there could be a further increase in the demand for pork.

The position for bacon and ham is now becoming fairly clear, with a sharp decline between 1970 and 1976. A continued slight fall in consumption seems fairly likely and a great deal depends on change in breakfast eating habits as well as price competition from other foods. Substitution of bacon for other meats at main meals during the day could help to balance the 'Continental breakfast' now widely eaten in UK homes and hotels.

TABLE 7. UK Meat Supplies 1979–80

Meat	% Home produced	% Imported
Beef and veal	84·0	16·0
Mutton and lamb	45·8	54·2
Pork	98·4	1·6
Bacon and ham	42·8	57·2
Poultry	99·1	0·9

The bacon market outlook at present remains complicated and distorted by the political and financial implications of the Common Agricultural Policy. In practice this has given certain countries—particularly Denmark and Holland—major advantages over the UK producer, in that pigmeat can be exported to the UK market with advantageous subsidies and favourable MCAs (Monetary Compensatory Amounts).

The UK producer captured less than 43 per cent of the total market in 1980 for bacon and ham, and the balance is made up as shown in Table 8.

TABLE 8. Imports of Bacon into the United Kingdom by Country of Origin
(000 tonnes)

	1972	%	1973	%	1974	%	1975	%	1976	%	1980	%
Denmark	263·2	75·2	248·6	77·6	241·4	80·9	232·0	80·7	208·1	77·3	207·8	68·2
Poland	38·0	10·9	32·2	10·1	19·4	6·5	18·4	6·4	16·6	6·1	18·2	5·8
Irish Republic	27·9	8·0	20·8	6·5	19·3	6·5	9·4	3·3	14·0	5·2	24·2	8·0
Sweden	10·0	2·9	7·5	2·3	5·1	1·7	4·3	1·5	1·1	0·4	1·0	0·3
Netherlands	8·6	2·4	9·7	3·0	12·0	4·0	21·1	7·3	25·5	9·5	45·4	15·0
Others	2·1	0·6	1·6	0·5	1·3	0·4	2·2	0·8	4·0	1·5	6·9	2·7
TOTAL	349·8	100·0	320·4	100·0	298·5	100·0	287·4	100·0	269·3	100·0	303·5	100·0

Source: Department of Trade.

This shows very clearly the dominant position of Denmark as a major supplier of bacon to the UK. Imports from Poland, which is outside the EEC, have declined, but these figures show the steady increase of imports from the Netherlands.

One clear trend over the past ten years in the UK has been the move away from the traditional Wiltshire whole-side cure. Various different cures have been developed, and much bacon is now sold in branded vacuum packs. Only part of the carcass is cured, and the meat can then be tailored for pork, ham and manufactured meat products.

Table 9 shows trends in the methods of disposal of pigs slaughtered in the UK. There is a marked decline in pigs used wholly for bacon and a steady percentage increase in pigs used in part for bacon. This reflects the rapid changes that have occurred in the curing and processing industry. The bacon factories are no longer exclusive users of the Wiltshire-type carcass. They are increasingly purchasing other types of cutter-pigs, and heavier pigs for the manufacture of sausages, pies and delicatessen, as well as a wide range of fresh pork meat.

TABLE 9. Bacon and Ham Production in the United Kingdom
('000 tonnes)

	1970	1972	1974	1976	1978	1979
Great Britain	176·2	202·6	182·7	180·1	169·7	158·3
of which:						
Wiltshire sides	95·0	108·6	93·6	101·6	90·2	79·0
Hams and gammons	30·8	39·2	33·0	31·9	37·7	37·9
Rolls (Ayrshire and other)	2·1	1·7	1·9	1·7	1·5	1·6
Any other bacon	48·3	53·0	54·2	44·9	40·3	39·8
Northern Ireland (unclassified)	74·4	73·7	60·6	42·0	43·9	49·7
United Kingdom	250·6	276·3	243·3	222·1	213·6	208·0

Source: MLC.

The working housewife has clearly shown her market requirements as far as pigmeat is concerned, and in short there seems to be an increasing demand for pre-packed convenience foods. This means that the market for pigmeat will be much more organised by retail outlets, who will exercise more influence on production methods, carcass weights and the quality of the meat. Without doubt the demand will be for lean meat. Percentage lean, the discoloration of fat, and the quality, texture, colour, and taste will be important.

OTHER BACKGROUND FACTORS TO PIGMEAT DEMAND

Demand for pigmeat must now be seen against a whole set of factors outside the range of the producer and processor. These factors include Common Agricultural Policy, the future on any incomes policy and the price, demand and competition of other meats.

The Meat and Livestock Commission are increasingly active in looking at trends in meat demand, and the following comments are based on extracts from the proceedings of a symposium held in April 1977 on Meat Demand and Price Forecasting.

Producers and all involved in pigmeat production, wholesaling and retailing must also consider the following factors:

1. Increased freezer ownership.
2. Increasing selling through supermarkets.
3. Use of meat in institutional catering.
4. Use of meat in manufacturing.
5. Competition from vegetable protein.
6. Meat promotion.
7. Health factors.

Increased Freezer Ownership

Estimates suggest that in 1976, 33 per cent of the United Kingdom households owned deep freezers (ie, deep freezers separate from refrigerators). It is forecast that 45–50 per cent of households will own deep freezers in 1985 and some would suggest even higher figures. Data from the National Food Survey results for 1972–5 suggest that households with deep freezers do not consume more carcass meat than non-freezer owning households; moreover, they tend to consume less processed meat. However, there may well have been considerable understatement in the National Food Survey figures. Nevertheless, a pattern emerges for individual meat categories. It seems that increased freezer ownership may be associated with higher pork consumption; the effect on beef, lamb and poultry meat appears neutral and there may be an adverse impact for bacon and ham.

Increased Selling Through Supermarkets

Sales of meat (by weight) through supermarkets in 1976 are thought to have accounted for 18–20 per cent of the meat sold through all retail outlets; estimates suggest that by 1985, 30–40 per cent of retail meat sales may be through supermarkets. This has important implications for the cutting and preparation of meat. The overall impact of this change in the retail selling pattern on meat consumption levels was thought to be marginally adverse for all categories of meat, mainly because there will be increased exposure of meat alongside competing food products.

Usage of Meat in Institutional Catering

There is very limited data to cover this field. Overall, it appears to have been a considerable growth area in terms of total turnover in the 1970s, particularly for such sectors as works' canteens. Some further growth in turnover is expected in the 1975–85 period but on a much more limited scale; moreover this is not likely to result in increased demand for meat. Local Authority spending on such items as school meals is likely to be an area where economies will be sought. For example, increased usage of meat substitutes may take place within recommended limits. The cheaper meats (e.g. poultry meat) and those which can be used for making into processed products (e.g. pork and beef) are likely to benefit at the expense of other meat items.

Usage of Meat in Manufacturing

In general, it is thought that processed meat products will form a higher share of the market in 1985 than in 1975—partly because of the continued switch towards convenience foods, but also because of the greater potential for economies in processing by use of meat extenders, etc. Recent studies suggest particular scope for expanded use of processed pigmeat and poultrymeat products. Morevoer, there is thought to be considerable further scope for processing beef. Lamb consumption is again likely to be adversely affected as a result of its limited use in processed products.

Competition from Vegetable Protein

This is thought likely to pose a substantial potential threat to meat consumption, partly because of the possibility of a substantial price advantage but also because vegetable protein products are being commended as being 'healthier'. The two main areas in which vegetable protein is likely to make an impact are:

(a) in the institutional catering sector, although further official recommendations and legislation are of importance here;

(b) as a meat extender in processed meat products.

The effect of increased usage of these products as meat extenders is by no means wholly adverse to total manufactured meat consumption, particularly for pigmeat which is more suitable for comminution and incorporation in a range of other processed products. Thus, the effect of vegetable protein is thought to be neutral in the pork sector but adverse for the other meat categories.

Meat Promotion

The 1978–85 period is likely to be a time when a substantally increased expenditure on meat promotion in the United Kingdom is going to take place compared with earlier periods. This is thought likely to have some favourable impact on meat consumption although the extent of this is impossible to estimate.

Health Factors

This is a complex issue which is very hard to judge over the foreseeable future. There has been increased publicity recently given to the contribution that consumption of animal fats might make to the incidence of coronary heart diseases. Also, there is increased attention given to 'dieting' in general. Experience from the United States as well as in the United Kingdom suggests that it is more likely to affect pork consumption adversely than consumption of other meats; this is because pork tends to be fatter than other meats.[1]

SELLING THE PIG

From an analysis of the market several factors emerge. There appears to be a demand for pork and fresh meat products but a static or declining market for bacon and ham. There are likely to be fewer market outlets, which will have increasing influence on type, quality and weight of pig produced.

[1] Extracts from proceedings of MLC Symposium on 'Meat Demand and Forecasting', April 1977.

External factors include the levels of income and points raised in in the previous section on the ownership of freezers, supermarkets, the competition from synthetic meats, and health factors.

TABLE 10. United Kingdom Pig Certifications by Method of Sales (%)

	1962	1968	1972	1974	1975	1979
Auction	21·5	14·0	12·9	11·2	10·4	8·8
Liveweight:						
Private sale	0·8	0·5	0·2	0·2	..	..
Ordinary deadweight:						
Centre	25·1	38·8	41·4	47·4	48·1	50·0
Bacon factories:						
Measured pigs	43·7	30·5	30·9	27·3	28·1	28·4
Other pigs	8·9	16·2	14·6	13·9	13·4	12·8
Total	100·0	100·0	100·0	100·0	100·0	100·0

.. Negligible

Table 10 shows the trends in methods of sale in recent years. The sale of pigs through auction marts has declined, and looks likely to continue to do so. Contracts between farmer and processor in some form or other are increasing and a large proportion of pigs sold to deadweight centres and measured pigs at bacon factories are traded by contract. These contracts are likely to be more flexible than fixed, and will be based on returns from the market.

Chapter 3

BASIC POLICY DECISIONS

WHEN CONSIDERING new units or the expansion of existing ones, there
are a number of basic policy decisions to be made. In the development
and growth of the pig industry there has been a tendency to take 'off the
cuff' or *ad hoc* decisions about new ventures and future planning. This
situation cannot continue, and the opportunity must be grasped to
stand back and look at fundamental issues. The main points for
consideration can be grouped under several headings as follows:

Statutory Regulations
- (a) Town and country planning.
- (b) River pollution.
- (c) Building regulations.
- (d) Safety and welfare recommendations.
- (e) Procedure.

Production Systems
- (a) Fresh meat.
- (b) Bacon.
- (c) Heavy pig.
- (d) Weaner production.
- (e) Weaner fattening.
- (f) Breeding stock multiplication.

Breeding
- (a) Market outlet influences.
- (b) Buying all replacements.
- (c) Breeding own replacements.
- (d) Closed herd policy.

Housing
- (a) Indoor or outdoor?
- (b) Solid manure or slurry system.
- (c) Intensive or semi-intensive.

Management
   (a) Age at weaning.
   (b) Purchased or home grown feeds?
   (c) Labour supply and continuity.

Capital Availability
   (a) Sources of finance.
   (b) Grants.

Statutory Regulations

In an increasingly organised and heavily populated country, there are certain regulations that the farming community must comply with. These are correct at the time of writing and the least that must be done when planning a unit is to check with local authorities about any special considerations that there may be or any recent changes in regulations.

Town and Country Planning 1971; also Town and Country Planning General Development Order 1973

'To ensure that the use of the buildings will not adversely affect others and that they will fit unobtrusively in the countryside.' All new buildings are subject to planning control but agricultural buildings on any farm over one acre are 'permitted' development except the following which require consent:

(a) Buildings within 24·4m of a trunk or classified road or which entail creating a new means of access to it.

(b) Buildings within 3·22km radius of a perimeter of an airfield which are more than 3m high.

(c) Buildings covering more than 464·5m^2 of ground.

(d) Buildings covering less than 464·5m^2 but within 91·4m of another building erected on the farm in the two preceding years and the total coverage of the two buildings exceeds 464·5m^2.

(e) Buildings over 12·1m in height.

In any of these cases three copies of plans and specifications must be submitted to Local Council to be considered by Planning Committees of local and County Councils. Consent may then be granted unconditionally, granted with conditions or refused. In certain circumstances a local planning authority may withdraw the general freedom from restriction and issue an Article 4 Direction. In this case consent is required. Moreover, in certain areas of high landscape value (such as National Parks) the local planning authority must be notified of the proposed erection of all new buildings and plans may be required.

Control of Pollution Act 1974

Much of the legislation on pollution has now been brought under the scope of the 1974 Act. Only certain parts of the Act are in force, so that some of the earlier legislation is still appropriate. A brief mention of the main Acts follow, but expert professional advice on legal matters may well be required in some cases.

(a) Rivers (Prevention of Pollution) Acts 1951 and 1961.
    The law states quite clearly that where any new discharge of foul water to a ditch, stream or river is planned, consent must be obtained from the local authority.

(b) Water Resources Act 1963.
    No pollution of underground water sources is permitted.

(c) Public Health Act 1936.
    This is concerned with causing of statutory nuisances, e.g. noise or smell.

(d) Common Law—do not cause nuisances that are actionable at Common Law.

(e) Public Health Act 1961.
    A farmer must be prepared to pay capital and annual charges where connections are made to the public sewer.

Building Regulations 1976

To ensure that the buildings will be structurally sound and safe, consent is required on all new buildings, and plans and outline specification must be submitted to the Local District Council. This is not subject to consideration by a Committee and after approval, cards have to be sent to the Council informing them of the progress of the building operation.

Health & Safety Act 1974, and Animal Welfare

New buildings must comply (where applicable) with the Agriculture (Safety of Workplaces) Regulations. Advice may be obtained from MAFF Safety Officers, who will also inspect new buildings on completion. Pig farmers would be well advised to refer to the Welfare Recommendations for Pigs (No. 2). This sets out quite clearly a set of standards and guides for the housing and management of pigs.

Procedure

The usual procedure when planning farm buildings is to list the requirements, establish the overall layout and design, organise the timing of the work and decide details of the construction, often with sketch plans. Outline estimates may be obtained from suppliers. This is followed by the preparation of detailed plans, specifications and the submission of quotations.

If necessary, apply to the Local Planning Authority for planning permission. Complete the application form for grant, submitting it, with plans, to the local office of the Ministry of Agriculture. To comply with the Building Regulations, plans must be sent to the Local Authority. The final estimates should be agreed with the builders and suppliers together with starting and completion dates. These details and evidence of Local Authority consents must be submitted to the Ministry of Agriculture for grant approval. Before giving the contractor the go-ahead, it is also advisable to check that all the necessary approvals have been obtained, including grant (MAFF) planning and building regulations (Local Authority) and tenants improvement (Landlord).

On the commencement of work submit a 'work' card to the Local Authority and inform the Ministry of Agriculture. Further cards must be sent to the Local Authority as the work proceeds. On completion payment will be made to the contractors less any retention sum. Submit the receipt with claim forms to the Ministry of Agriculture for payment of grant. A final inspection will be made before payment. Six months after completion, the retention sum will be paid to the contractor.

If the work is being organised by a surveyor or architect, inspection will normally be made at all stages, and he should be kept informed of progress.

Where a grant is applied for, on no account should work be started before approval has been given.

Production Systems

Obviously any business venture will need to ensure a secure outlet for its final product. This basic policy decision will dictate and influence other policy matters, especially housing and management. The following market options need to be considered, and will in turn lead to choice of production systems:

(a) Fresh meat.

(b) Bacon.

(c) Heavy pig.

(d) Weaner sales.

(e) Breeding stock multiplication.

It is probable that under EEC conditions the cyclical movements of the pig market will continue and may even be exaggerated and producers will need to secure long term contracts from individual processors and factories.

B

(a) Fresh Meat

Pigs for this market could be offered at a wide range of weights from 59kg liveweight as a light porker, to a cutter at 72 to 77kg, or through to a pig for part curing and manufacturing at 100kg liveweight. The best choice for optimum output through a given set of buildings may be a combination of these weights, say 20 per cent at pork and 80 per cent as cutter. In any case the carcase is certainly likely to be graded which indicates some form of restricted feeding. This in turn will influence house design, capacity and feeding system. For the fresh meat trade some boars of the newer imported breeds such as the Hampshire may be considered so that there will be interactions on the breeding programme.

(b) Bacon

A very specialist market, mainly for the Wiltshire whole cure trade. Where carcase quality is good, specialist bacon production has consistently shown best results in terms of profitability when measured by the Cambridge Pig Management Scheme results. The requirements from a production viewpoint will be similar to those for fresh meat production but with a more limited weight range of about 86 to 95kg liveweight. This in turn will affect house design, feed systems and animal throughput. From results recorded at Pig Performance Testing Stations it would appear that the best breeding for bacon production will be the native Large White, the Welsh and the Landrace, or a planned cross breeding programme using two or three of these breeds. Of all commercial systems bacon production probably makes the highest demand from a management point of view.

(c) Heavy Pig

A specialist operation closely tied to one or two large meat-processing companies, the whole system being well developed through a supply of specialist breeding stock. At the present time there is no restriction on fat depth, so that in certain situations where cereals, by-products and swill are available this type of production may be an obvious choice. Securing a contract for the end product will be a first consideration, and house design for feeding pigs can be very simple and lead to savings in fixed capital investment.

However, the system is really geared to one type of pig production and is much less flexible than the fresh meat or bacon options which are capable of some interchangeability. According to the Cambridge figures, heavy pig production has been on the whole not as profitable as other types of fattening operations—particularly in the past two or three years.

(d) (1) Weaner Production

An attractive proposition, especially at the present time. Capital investment is usually lower for weaner production than for a breeding and feeding herd. Concentration on the breeding herd selling weaners at 25–30kg liveweight has been shown to be probably the next most profitable operation to producing baconers. Thus weight and age form a natural break in housing requirements since weaners can be kept in rearing accommodation until point of sale. A central system geared to a basic weight—usually 18kg—followed by sliding scale is often the best business arrangement, with prices linked to end product fatstock prices. This type of operation has often been encouraged by feed compounders and weaner group operations, which may ease working capital requirements. Once this breeding operation has been firmly established, it is often then possible to add a feeding unit to complete the fattening of the pig at a later stage.

(d) (2) Weaner Purchasing and Fattening

Still a fairly widespread practice with a strong regional and traditional bias. A good example of this is the Welsh weaners that are produced on the small border farms and then moved to Midland areas around Birmingham for finishing on swill or other by-product feeds. This type of operation is now less prevalent as most large new units are geared to a breeding and feeding system on the same farm.

Moving weaners always involves health risks and usually causes problems unless it is part of a well organised co-operative weaner scheme where several breeding units may be sending pigs to a large central fattening unit. TGE and SVD have caused problems for this type of pig production, and the tightening up of regulations about swill preparation and feeding, and movement of pigs, will only cause a further reduction in this type of trade.

(e) Breeding Stock Multiplication

This is a comparatively recent introduction, and has become important as breeding companies require close control and rapid multiplication of their 'seedstock'. The structure of the MLC Breed Improvement Scheme has also given some impetus to this type of operation. Normally there is a binding legal contract to produce a specified number of gilts per year, with cull gilts and male pigs sold for slaughter. Control is usually fairly rigid and technical staff from the parent company will often be involved in the first selection of breeding stock for sale. Housing and management obviously need to be first class, and special facilities may be needed for on-farm performance testing.

Male and female stock are usually provided for multiplication of crossbred gilts, and for control and recording purposes the multiplier herd will not often exceed the 200 sow mark. From a financial point of view the multiplication can show an extremely good return on capital, but it requires a very special and meticulous approach at all stages of pig production.

Breeding

Market outlet will again influence choice, and for *ad lib*-fed manufacturing pigs it may be possible to use a pig bred specially for this market. Walls Livestock Limited (now Masterbreeders), who have been breeding stock for the manufacturing trade for over twenty years, have introduced a hybrid gilt which has been bred to give low-cost weaners for all markets.

The breed choice for other types of pig production will clearly be the Large White, Welsh or Landrace, with some of the recently introduced breeds, crossbreds or synthetic lines also available for consideration.

Purchasing All Requirements

At the present time this is fast becoming a main choice, with up to one-fifth of the national herd bought in on a 'flying herd' basis. Hybrid gilts are normally brought onto the producer's farm as maidens at pre-arranged dates to fit into a planned batch farrowing programme. Females are usually first cross and are mated back to Landrace or Large White boars for meat production. Certainly by doing this, the farmer can concentrate on his own production and management methods, and can probably influence his profitability better by doing this than by worrying about selecting breeding stock.

A fairly rapid turnover of breeding stock will ensure that he keeps progressively up to date with genetic improvements being made at nucleus herd level. The only reservation can be about health risks, but this can be minimised by restricting his purchases to one company or organisation and to a particular multiplier with good sound health record.

Breeding Own Crossbred Replacements

This system involves the establishment of a small purebred nucleus herd and by the use of AI, or high pointed boars and natural service, crossbred females are produced at home. This is a pattern demonstrated by the National Agricultural Centre Pig Unit with considerable success. The normal ratio of nucleus to crossbred parent would be 1:10, so that a small purebred herd of 25–30 sows would maintain a commercial herd of 250 sows. This would mean bringing about 10–12 gilts onto the farm annually, which certainly reduces the health risks when compared with purchasing all hybrid gilts as described earlier.

There is still a good deal of complicated recording and management, but scope exists for breed improvement with the use of AI, and flexibility can be maintained by changing breeds and strains. Some on-farm performance testing will be essential for crossbred gilt selection, but I believe with larger units this will often be the preferred method of obtaining breeding stock replacements.

Closed Herd Policy

For a reduction in health risks this will be the obvious choice. Use would be made of AI on the male side and if crossbred stock were required, two female nucleus lines would be needed. A large herd

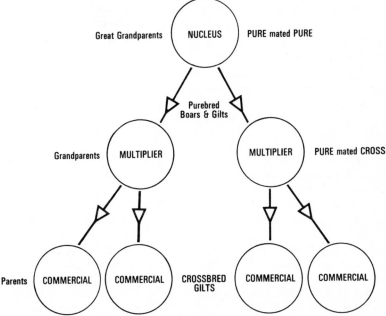

FIG. 1. *Diagrammatic layout for Breeding Company—breed improvement programme.*

would be essential to follow this type of programme and size will generally rule the choice out. A working knowledge of genetics would be required as well as management and recording skills. A small herd will not possess the gene pool essential for breed improvement, and the herd may fall behind contemporary progress very quickly. The large capital investment in housing and feed would then be wasted, or at least not used to best advantage.

Variations on this policy, such as a rotational crossing programme, have been worked out, but again two breeds are involved with some boar purchase (or AI). There is a large amount of work involved in selection and testing and to do the job well individual feeding facilities are necessary for testing stock.

Housing

(a) Indoor or Outdoor?

Geographical location will often settle this question outright, coupled with soil type and rainfall. On light land in the South and East and occasionally on chalk soil outdoors units continue to flourish. A report from Wye College shows that on a comparative basis outdoor pig production can be very profitable. However, a survey by Parrish of large units did not arrive at the same conclusion (*Big Farm Management*, Oct, Nov, Dec 1972). The trend is quite clearly towards intensive units and this is even apparent in formerly arable areas—the East Yorkshire situation has already been quoted as an example of this.

(b) Straw or Slurry?

Housing systems will now largely be influenced by the ability to handle muck in a solid or liquid form. This is the starting point for many new units and also for expansion plans in some cases. This major decision will have interactions on building type and layout and on the siting of the unit. Town and Country Planning permission will need consideration at this early stage and will possibly dictate policy.

From almost ten years of work at the NAC Pig Unit the choice appears to narrow down to two main housing systems. These, of course, will have variations as there are a host of profitable types of housing which suit particular individuals and localities.

It is very important to stand back and see the choice in perspective. Of the two systems suggested one (B) is for arable situations where straw is available. Housing is based on group systems, general purpose buildings and mechanical handling of manure, probably returning it to an arable enterprise.

During pregnancy sows are housed in groups in yards or cubicles, farrowed in maternity rooms, which are followed by group suckling on straw. Feeding is completed in a straw-bedded, trough-fed general-purpose house. System A assumes the ability to handle slurry and so is based on slats and individual housing of the sow during pregnancy in stalls or tethers. Farrowing takes place in a maternity section, and rearing and fattening in partially slatted floor housing. Details of design, layout and operation of these basic choices will be found in later sections of this book.

Management

(a) Purchased or Home Grown Feeds?

This decision will often have been pre-empted by the type of unit. Arable-based systems will often have home-grown cereals available for use with a concentrate. Intensive units on limited acreage will almost of necessity be compounded users. A decision is vital at the outset, although it is probably easier to add feed preparation equipment rather than to let it become idle. Staff and labour requirements will have

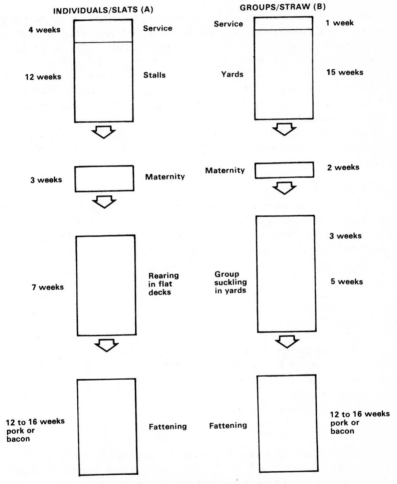

FIG. 2. *Two Main Housing Systems*

some influence and it may well become a choice between on-farm feed preparation or on-farm selection of replacement breeding stock.

Size of operation may allow advantageous buying of compounds, and integration with other farm enterprises may strengthen this position. Whatever the choice, and this will be more fully explored in the Feeding section of this book, the decision must be based on a rational and budgeted view of the prevailing situation, and a constant review will be needed.

(b) Labour

This is perhaps the limiting factor on many large-scale units. Size and scope of the unit and the production system will decide the number of men required and the conditions they will operate under. A specialist team of three or four men is probably the best solution, but this can only be justified on a large unit. An increasing number of trained specialists are coming into the pig husbandry field from practically-based sandwich courses at training colleges. They will need attractive salaries, good working conditions, a settled domestic background, status, with perhaps some initial on-farm training. These are the key personnel in our industry in the years ahead, a factor that is only now being recognised.

(c) Age of Weaning

This is a basic management decision that has been under review in the last year or so. In 1970 the great bulk of the national herd was still weaned at five weeks, a surprising amount at about eight weeks, with a relatively small handful at four weeks or earlier.

Herds Over 500 pigs	UK 1970	Scottish Survey (120 Herds)
Below 4 weeks	7%	10%
5–6 weeks	48%	56%
7–8 weeks	44%	34%

Recent surveys have shown that many specialist units have now moved to three-week weaning. Attempts at weaning earlier than this— say, 7 to 10 days—have not been commercially successful. My estimate at the present time would be that producers would fall into the following categories:

Below 4 weeks	40%
5–6 weeks	50%
7–8 weeks	10%

There is clearly greater potential with early weaning systems than is at present being realised, but expert management, correct nutrition, and attention to detail are essential to realise this potential. The development of the flat deck system has perhaps been the most important factor in recent years in the trend towards three-week weaning.

Capital Availability and Requirements

This is always the starting point for new units and for expansion plans, and this will be explored in greater depth in the appropriate section of this book. Sources of finance are listed in many of the booklets published by the banks and the usual criteria for borrowing for a farm business are set out.

GOVERNMENT AND STATUTORY AID—CAPITAL GRANTS
Farm and Horticultural Development Scheme

This scheme is designed to enable farmers and growers whose incomes are below the national average for non-agricultural industry to obtain grants in respect of development plans to improve their holdings and achieve a 'comparable income'.

(1) Applicants, or the person effectively in charge of the applicant's business, must have had at least five years' experience in the industry or hold an appropriate certificate from a recognised teaching establishment. At least half their income must be derived from agriculture and at least half their working time derived from it.

(2) Applicants are required to submit a development plan designed to raise the income to the appropriate level within six years, while employing at least one man working full-time.

(3) The present earned income (defined below) must not exceed £3,300 per labour unit. A labour unit is the amount of work done by a full-time worker, 2,200 hours/year. Earned income is broadly profit, plus labour costs, interest charges, notional rent in the case of owner occupiers, and expenditure on 'landlord's capital'. Certain other adjustments for depreciation and return on tenant's capital are made. Eligibility may be determined either on actual accounts, or by means of standard outputs from the farm's particular enterprises and full details are available in the explanatory leaflets.

Applications where incomes are already at or above this level may be accepted providing the unit is 'at risk'—i.e. liable to fall below the comparative level. Grant levels are 20 per cent lower for 'at risk' holdings with a minimum grant of 8 per cent.

(4) The limits of expenditure for which grants may be approved are above £1,000 per plan and below £25,167 per labour unit. Pig production enterprises must spend between £6,295 and £31,913 and furthermore must on completion of the plan be able to supply 35 per cent of feedingstuff requirements. For livestock, the grant only applies to additional animals, and excludes replacements, dealing activities, short-term keep, etc. Also net sales of animal produce must account for more than 60 per cent of farm sales, less livestock purchases.

(5) Under the FHDS, records have to be produced and submitted annually as a condition of the scheme. Grants for record-keeping

are payable, but will cease upon the completion of the approved plan and will not in any case exceed four years.

(6) The farmer can choose to have the grant based on: the actual cost of the work (a test will be made to ensure that it is not unreasonably high—if it is, the grant may be reduced), or on a standard cost for certain work, or a combination of actual and standard costs. Details of standard costs determined by the Ministry are available in leaflets obtainable from divisional offices. Detailed information on the FHDS, explanatory leaflets and application forms are obtainable from the Ministry's divisional offices. Prior consent is imperative before work starts.

(7) In certain cases it may be possible to obtain a free loan through the Agricultural Credit Corporation Limited, in support of an application to a bank for funds to carry out an approved scheme. Also, FHDS applicants are granted priority where land given up under outgoer's schemes comes up for sale.

Grant rates vary, and those listed below are only examples. Special rates for less favoured areas are in brackets.

	Agriculture	
Permanent buildings	25%	(30)%
Yards, platforms, etc	25%	(30)%
Waste disposal	25%	(30)%
Gas & electricity supplies	25%	(30)%
Water supplies	25%	(50)%
Road works, etc	25%	(50)%
Fences etc, land clearance	25%	(50)%
Livestock purchase	10%	(15)%
Plant and machinery purchase	10%	(15)%
Preparation of development plans	25%	(25)%

FARM CAPITAL SCHEME 1973

This scheme applies to the United Kingdom. Capital expenditure on a wide range of items is eligible for grant. The main items for the pig farmer are as follows: farm buildings, yards, farm waste disposal, roads, bridges, gas and electricity, water supply, fences and hedges, gates and walls. Grant is not payable on repairs, maintenance, temporary or makeshift works, or for plant and machinery with the exception of certain items used in connection with water and electricity supply.

Grants may be based on either actual or standard costs or a combination of both. The standard rate is 20 per cent.

Applications must cover at least £400 of eligible expenditure, but this can be made up of several items. There is an upper limit of £25,167 per labour unit on the aggregate of expenditure which may be grant-aided in respect of any particular agricultural business under this scheme, the Farm and Horticultural Development Scheme and the Horticultural Capital Scheme in a period of two consecutive years.

Investments in pig production will only qualify if they amount to more than £6,295 and less than £31,913 and if the holding will be capable of producing 35 per cent of the feed required for the pigs after the grant-aided work has been carried out.

The main conditions for grant are that the expenditure must be for farming purposes and the cost must not be unreasonable for the intended agricultural purposes. To qualify for grant on the full range of items the farm business must be capable, after the grant-aided work has been carried out, of yielding a net annual income of at least £2,900.

Unlike the FHDS scheme there is a three-month delay in payment of the FCGS grant after it has been agreed.

(Detailed information on the 1973 Farm Capital Grant Scheme, explanatory leaflets and application forms are available from the Ministry's divisional offices. In all cases the Ministry's written approval must be obtained before work is started.)

OTHER GRANTS

Training Grants

Subject to certain conditions, the Agricultural Training Board provides grants to offset, at least partially, the direct costs incurred by farmers and growers when they or their employees (if any) take part in training in skills related to agricultural and horticultural production activities. Within specified limits the Board also reimburses subsistence and travelling expenses for attendance at courses of practical training or relevant further education. The broad categories of training covered by the ATB grants are as follows:

(1) Career training-grants for training apprentices; grants for training students during the industrial period of sandwich courses; grants to support attendance at courses of further education related to the work on the holding.

(2) Established worker training-grants for off-the-job training, including attendance at approved courses held away from the holding.

(3) Training systems and methods—grants to groups of agricultural and horticultural businesses formed for training purposes as formally constituted but unincorporated associations registered with the Board; grants for training suitable people as training officers or instructors; grants for employing training officers and instructors. The rates of grant payable are fixed for a twelve-month period from 1st August each year.

(Details of current rates may be obtained from Agricultural Training Board, Bourne House, 32-34 Beckenham Road, Beckenham, Kent BR3 4PB.)

AGRICULTURAL AND HORTICULTURAL CO-OPERATION

A wide range of Government grants exists to assist with the promotion, organisation and carrying out of co-operative activities in agriculture and horticulture.

Administered by the Central Council for Agricultural and Horticultural Co-operation, various schemes provide not only grant assistance for co-operative activities in marketing and production on the same basis as individual farmers and growers, but also grant aid towards the costs incurred by co-operatives in undertaking certain activities, which individual farmers and growers would not normally be expected to undertake.

Only proposals approved by the Central Council may qualify for assistance and in each case the rate of grant to be paid is subject to the Council's discretion. The Council takes into account the constitution of the co-operatives association, members' commitment or proposed commitment to the project, its economic worthwhileness, and the activity in which the co-operative association is or will be engaged.

(Details: Central Council for Agricultural and Horticultural Co-operation, 301–344 Market Towers, New Covent Garden Market, 1 Nine Elms Lane, London SW8 5NQ.)

Capital Requirements

It is difficult to be precise about exact capital requirements for a pig unit. It is much easier to budget for a new unit perhaps than to expand an existing one, but this will be considered in detail in the section on Recording and Management Control. However, to give some indication

CAPITAL COSTS

Housing and Services	Total £	Per Sow £
(a) 250 Sows and Progeny Dry Sows, Farrowing, Rearing and Fattening Housing	174,000	696
(b) Roads, Services and Office Facilities	18,000	72
(c) Feeding Equipment, Machinery	12,000	48
	£204,000	816
Livestock		
250 Gilts at £120	30,000	
10 Boars at £250	2,500	
	£32,500	130
Working Capital		
Feed, Labour, Miscellaneous Costs	86,400	345
TOTAL	£322,900	£1,291

of initial capital requirements I am going to make some assumptions for a 250-sow unit producing bacon pigs. The housing and management would be based on an intensive system using slatted floors on a new site. No allowances are made for land purchase or staff housing, but a four-man team would be employed. Compound feeds would be bought in bulk and crossbred gilts, boars and replacement stock purchased from a breeding company.

A cash flow would show that peak capital requirements would be reached in the 10th and 11th months of the first year of operation.

All construction work is undertaken by contractors' staff.

Prefabricated buildings are used throughout, and calculations have been based on prices current in January 1980.

Capital requirements must, of course, be related to working capital, cash flow, profits and return on capital. A full explanation and breakdown of the financial aspects of a large pig unit will be found in a later section of this book.

Chapter 4

BREEDING

DURING THE past ten years there has been a concentration and specialisation in the breeding of pigs. Genetic improvement has been taking place at a rapid pace, and the present structure of breed improvement is based upon the MLC Pig Improvement Scheme on the one hand, and a number of commercial breeding organisations on the other.

MLC PIG IMPROVEMENT SCHEME

A breed improvement scheme based on a two-tier herd system was implemented by MLC in 1966, and incorporated much of the thinking and spadework which had been carried out by PIDA from its inception in 1964. However, because of changes within the industry, recommendations from two Pig Study Groups that had reported in 1970 were adopted in the introduction of the Pig Improvement Scheme launched in April 1971. Breeding herds were categorised into four main groups:

        (1) Nucleus herds.
        (2) Reserve nucleus herds.
        (3) Nucleus multiplier herd.
        (4) The breeding company.

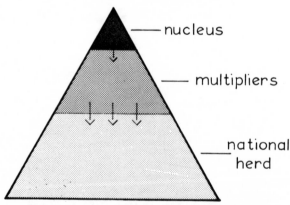

FIG. 3. *Breed improvement—pyramidical structure.*

Basically, the pyramidical structure of the industry was advocated, with breed improvement being spearheaded by the nucleus herd and improved breeding stock being distributed within the National Herd by a multiplication system. Performance and progeny testing are the main tools for breed improvement with selection based on traits of economic importance, mainly feed conversion efficiency and the production of lean meat.

Nucleus Herds

The Pig Improvement Scheme Yearbook 1978–79 lists 59 nucleus herds with the following breed breakdown:

Large White	29
Landrace	24
Welsh	5
Gloucester Old Spot	1

The nucleus herds are selected from within the purebred population and tested intensively. They include herds formerly classified as Elite under the Accreditation Scheme, of which many were formerly the pedigree breeding herds which were an integral part of the breed industry in the first half of this century.

Rapid generation turnover in the nucleus herds is practised and with the use of tested boars genetic progress is maximised. Groups of young boars are forwarded to MLC for central testing, whilst gilts are tested on the farm.

National boar-testing facilities are reserved for nucleus herds and the central boar performance test, or combined test, is designed to measure a young boar's potential for siring profitable progeny. The test, which is highly competitive, involves the breeding herd in submitting large numbers of groups to MLC testing stations.

The test group, comprising four pigs all from one litter, is made up of two entire boars, one castrate and one gilt. Each pair of boars is housed in a kennel-type house. The boars lie together but are fed separately so that feed consumption can be accurately recorded. The castrate and gilt (sibs) are housed in a fully enclosed building and fed together.

The pigs enter the testing station when their individual weights are between 18 and 25kg. The test starts when each boar weighs 27kg and the sibs' weights total 54kg. The test is completed when each boar weighs 91kg and the sibs' total weight is 181kg, at which time the sibs are slaughtered. Detailed carcase measurements are taken and a sample joint is fully dissected into lean, fat and bone.

Feed consumption, liveweight gain and ultrasonically-measured fat depths are recorded on each boar. This information is combined with feed consumption, growth records from the sibs, plus their carcase measurements, and expressed on a selection index as a points score for each boar. The average score is always maintained at 100 points although the actual performance of boars in the testing station is steadily improving.

Boars scoring below 90 points are slaughtered and licensed boars over 90 points are offered back to the breeder. Boars in the 90–120 points range are readily available, and if used over a period, will give real improvements in the herd. Boars scoring over 120 points occur less frequently and are therefore in greater demand. Those scoring over 160 points are usually retained in the nucleus herd or enter an AI stud.

Combined testing is a fundamental part of the life of the nucleus breeder and results are taken into account when an independent selection panel meets annually to review the categories. The reserve nucleus herd may be moved into the nucleus herd category on application, after testing of some of their stock at MLC testing stations. Both nucleus and reserve herds must be members of the Government Pig Health Scheme.

The Nucleus Multiplier Herd

The multiplying herd operates by taking the gilts and tested boars from nucleus herds and multiplying these for commercial herds. The usual pattern is to produce a first-cross gilt for sale, though occasionally it may be a purebred pig. Quite often multipliers will be linked quite closely with specific nucleus herds for crossbred gilt production. Members of the Pig Improvement Multiplication Scheme agree to specific conditions about the sources of their stock and are members of the Government Pig Health Scheme.

Gilt selection in both nucleus and multiplier herds will often be based on the MLC on-farm test. Growth rate is measured along with ultra-sonic testings, visual inspection of legs and action, teat numbers and spacings, and with overall conformation assessment this should provide a good improved breeding gilt capable of producing five or six litters during her working life.

ON-FARM TESTING

MLC test about 70,000 pigs a year on the farm. Some of these are boars but most are gilts.

The test consists of an operator regularly visiting farms and measuring fat depths of live pigs by means of an ultrasonic machine. Potential breeding pigs of between 68–113kg liveweight are so tested.

The fat measurements are taken at fixed points (P_1 and P_2) over the eye muscle at the last rib and at the shoulder and loin. The P_1 and P_3 figures are combined with figures of weight for age to give a simple index score for each pig.

Many factors besides genetic differences can influence both weight for age and fatness under farm conditions—the prevailing weather conditions, type of ration, housing, and health of pigs. To overcome this problem, index scores are based on a rolling herd average from *either* a total of 40 or more pigs *or* on all pigs measured within the previous six weeks. Averages are calculated only within the same breed and sex, while the score is based on the herd average and standard deviation. The average score is always 10 points and the range usually —20 to + 40. Once again, the higher score the better the pig.

Pigs with the same score are of the same merit relative to their herd contemporaries. Therefore, selection above a given score will result in a given proportion of animals tested being retained. (For example, 20 points and above is equivalent to a selection intensity of 1 in 6.) But because herds differ in genetic merit, between herd comparisons should not be made. Many factors can influence both growth and fatness under farm conditions—the prevailing weather conditions, type of ration, housing, health of pig, as well as genetic differences. For this reason comparisons between pigs should be made only within a batch measured at the same time, and reared under similar conditions, on the same farm. The average score of the batch should be calculated and only pigs that have scored above average should be considered for purchase. It is not sensible to compare index scores achieved on different farms.

COMMERCIAL HERDS

The commercial pig farmer will buy first-cross gilts from the nucleus multiplier, along with tested boars, to produce pigs for slaughter. The first-cross gilt shows a marked superiority in litter productivity to the purebred gilt, and feed conversion efficiency and carcase quality will usually be the average of the performance of the two purebred parent breeds. Further reference to this is made in the section on cross-breeding. Of course, the success of the Pig Improvement Scheme is measured by increased profitability in the commercial herd. Some indication of the improvement that has taken place in the past few years is indicated by an MLC survey in 1969. This showed that 34 per cent of all boars licensed were from herds in the Accreditation Scheme and each year approximately five million slaughter pigs were sired by scheme boars through AI or natural service.

As a further check that purebred pigs from herds in the scheme are better than those from commercial herds, samples of commercial purebred are purchased regularly for comparison. Results of these comparative tests indicate a cash advantage of £1·80 extra per pig from progeny of scheme purebreds.

CROSSBREEDING AND HYBRIDISATION

MLC have been involved in breed improvement since the mid-sixties and a Working Party was appointed in the spring of 1976 to examine and comment on the progress and current position of the MLC testing programme, and the best use of national stations.

The Working Party report was published in June 1977, from which the following extracts are taken on several specific points.

(1) Central Testing

The group recommend that no immediate steps should be taken to limit the operation of the central testing stations, though we believe that the emphasis will change. There will be a decreasing role for the Commission to test pigs for individual breeders at central testing stations, but there should be an increase in authenticating results from an accreditation scheme. Although recognising the changing situation in regard to central testing, the group recommend that it should continue in its present form with only minor changes for a period of at least three years, when the situation will need to be reviewed again in the light of changes in the structure of the industry and the level of demand.

(2) On-farm Testing

The importance of on-farm testing programmes within individual units is growing and is an acceptable method for selecting breeding stock. The present Commission service is fulfilling the needs of a number of nucleus breeders and is worthwhile, and should continue, but more emphasis should be given to the application of results. The Commission should continue to offer a technical service, modestly subsidised, and continue to encourage the development of more accurate forms of on-farm testing.

(3) Accreditation

It is recommended that the Commission should introduce a new accreditation scheme with access controlled by the Independent Selection Panel. Accreditation should involve authentication of breeding stock recording systems, herd health and performance levels.

(4) Herd Health

The health arrangements in relation to central testing have worked satisfactorily in recent years and it is recommended that such arrangements continue. They reflect credit on participators and operators. While the Government Health Scheme may change in detail, the Commission is recommended to watch closely any alteration which might restrict freedom of action by herds within the scheme and should ensure that as far as reasonably possible they are not put at a long-term disadvantage compared with herds outside the scheme. Herd health authentication is a desirable goal, but may cause difficulties for certain herds.

(5) *Method of Testing*

There is an urgent need for alternative systems of testing to be evaluated. In particular a system of testing which involves feeding to a scale and aims at selecting pigs with maximum lean tissue feed conversion ratios requires investigation. This is an area of direct concern to the whole breeding industry and the Commission should take the lead in ensuring that the necessary development work is undertaken.

PLANNED CROSS-BREEDING

Much of the impetus for breed improvement in the last few years has come from the widespread adoption of planned crossbreeding. The crossbred sow has been a cornerstone of pigmeat production for many years, and a great deal of practical expertise and considerable scientific investigation has shown that hybrid vigour obtained in crossbred animals results in a better breeding performance and more pigs per litter.

The progeny of crossbred dams are more robust and are more viable feeding pigs than are the progeny of purebred dams.

Generally speaking, however, hybrid vigour gives improvement only in those characteristics which are weakly inherited. Numbers born and reared and weight of pigs at three and eight weeks—all weakly inherited characteristics—are improved when crossbred dams are used. But, so far as the moderately and highly inherited traits are concerned, cross-breeding does not automatically give any advantage. In the case of such highly important economic characteristics as food conversion ratio, growth rate and lean meat content of the carcase, the crossbred progeny's potential will generally be around the average of the two parents. It is therefore vitally important to use only parent stock having a known high genetic potential for such traits. The better the parents in this respect, the better the progeny are likely to be, and this highlights the role of the nucleus herd within the MLC scheme. It is of vital importance to maintain the purebred parent lines, a job which is also being carried out by some of the commercial breeding organisations.

BREEDING ORGANISATIONS

Large-scale breeding organisations first came into prominence in the early 1960s, and their growth has been a feature of the industry over the past ten years. In some cases experience of breeding methods was obtained in other livestock spheres and in particular the poultry world.

These pig-breeding companies fall into several groups. Wall's were one of the first in the field and are a good example of one group which provided selected breeding stock to farmers and guaranteed to buy back the product under contract, for use in their convenience and manufactured food outlets. Other food processors have followed their example.

The animal food compounders form a second major group and in some cases have developed crossbred gilts as part of an integrated market scheme. This also helped to maintain and safeguard their share of the feedingstuffs market.

A third and largest group have become established as specialist breeding companies supplying hybrid gilts and selected boars on the national market. A good example of this type of operation is provided by Pig Improvement Company, who were established in 1962. Another illustration of this type of operation is provided by Northern Pig Development Company Ltd. The original Landrace herd was part of the MLC scheme, but after the formation of the company testing facilities were developed of their own and they now produce a large number of hybrid gilts through their fully owned multiplication farms throughout the UK.

A recent feature in this field has been the grouping together of individual pig breeders to form breeding companies such as United Pig Breeders Ltd and Premier Pig Testing Company, and this trend seems likely to continue. A register of these companies appears in MLC Pig Improvement Yearbook 1976/77, along with general remarks as supplied by the companies. Over 20 companies now appear in the Herd Book, with a brief description of their activities.

All these companies test and select their pigs by a variety of methods, some of them under the MLC umbrella using central testing facilities, sib testing, carcase evaluation and on-farm testing. Other organisations will test privately but using the same criteria of growth rate, feed efficiency and carcase quality. Pure breed improvement is usually undertaken with one or two nucleus herds from which tested stock are transferred to contract multiplication units. Selected crossbred females and boars are then sold to commercial producers.

Health controls are usually applied with some companies offering only MD stock. Most companies will normally have a carefully planned breed improvement scheme monitored by their own geneticist or consultant. This section of the industry has become highly organised and competitive, and has exploited the market opportunities that exist with the formation of large-scale commercial units. Sales estimates include 9,000 boars, more than 8,000 purebred gilts, and up to 66,000 crossbred gilts a year. This could influence up to two million pigs slaughtered annually.

By comparison, the 60 independent nucleus, 30 reserve nucleus and 70 nucleus multiplier herds in the MLC pig improvement scheme sell annually about 5,000 boars, 8,000 purebred gilts and 10,000 crossbred gilts. These figures indicate that about 30 per cent of all replacement females and 90 per cent of boars are bought in from breeding companies or herds involved in MLC schemes.

TESTING HYBRID PIGS

How good are these new hybrids or crossbreds? This is the question that most commercial producers have asked from time to time. And how do they compare with those produced from within the MLC Pig Improvement Scheme? With a growing number of different hybrids on offer, there is an increasing need for factual information on the performance of these animals. The Report of the MLC Commercial Pig Study Group in 1969 described a scheme entitled 'commercial product evaluation' under which representative samples of slaughter generation pigs would be tested. This plan was put into action by MLC at Celyn Farm in North Wales and started in September 1972.

The object of the test is to provide objective information on the reproductive performance of hybrid crossbred gilts currently on offer to the market. The growth rate and carcase quality of their progeny will also be tested to several weights for pork, cutter, bacon and heavy pigs. The pigs will be fed at two different levels, restricted and *ad lib*, and dissection of carcases will be carried out for evaluation work.

Thirty hybrid gilts and seven boars are purchased each year on a random basis from each of nine companies and housed under commercial conditions at the MLC's Celyn Farm, Northop, Clwyd. The test is based on the results of two litters per female; approximately 200 of the progeny from each company are fed to three different weights— 61kg, 91kg and 118kg—and on two feed treatments, restricted and *ad libitum*.

The reproductive performance is fully recorded to provide information on number of piglets born and reared, and weaning weights. Feed conversion ratios, daily liveweight gain and carcase measurements are recorded for the feeding pigs. A proportion of pigs at all weights are fully dissected. The company pigs are compared with each other and with purebred pigs.

It is now clear that the general principles of this form of evaluation are valuable and in the interests of the industry, but that only a few pig-breeding companies and organisations can be evaluated at any one time. A pattern appears to be establishing, with a few companies performing consistently well, and most hybrids outperforming the Large White sample—although the purebreds would not be expected to perform as well as the crossbreds in reproductive traits.

The accumulation of results of several years is probably the most important aspect of commercial product evaluation, but in fact there were few significant differences between the performances of most companies.

Results from Pigs Purchased 1975–78

The average number of pigs born alive per litter was 10·6, and the average number of pigs reared to weaning at five weeks of age was 9·5 which is well above the average of the top third of MLC-recorded herds. As expected, the crossbred dams produced and reared more piglets than the purebreds. Average piglet weight at weaning was 9·0kg, and feed consumed by dam and litter per kg of piglet produced averaged 5·2kg.

Average growth rate for pigs slaughtered at 87kg and fed *ad lib* was 835g per day while pigs fed on a restricted scale averaged 653g per day. Average feed conversion ratio was 2·87 which is better than the average of the top third of MLC-recorded herds.

The average P_2 fat depth for pigs slaughtered at 87kg, which included pigs fed *ad lib*, was 16·0mm, and the average lean in carcase was 49·6 per cent.

Results showing the relative performance of each company for different characteristics are published annually in a test report. Full details of management and veterinary procedures, carcase evaluation and statistical analysis are given in *Commercial Pig Evaluation* and *Commercial Pig Evaluation: Management and Procedures*. Both publications cost £2 and are available from MLC's Public Relations Department.

As the tests proceed and results accumulate a great deal of information and evidence will be available to help the farmer in selecting a breeding organisation from which to buy his breeding replacements. In the meantime the results should be interpreted with care. Other factors such as health status, price, availability, or the technical back-up services provided could all help in making the final decision.

ARTIFICIAL INSEMINATION

AI has been widely used in the pig industry with a history going back over 30 years. In spite of vigorous promotion by MLC in recent years, growth of its use has been disasppointing, with less than 3 per cent of the national herd accounted for.

With insemination services the conception rate appears to be about 77 per cent, which is difficult to compare with the natural service as no national figure is calculated.

Disadvantages and Difficulties

AI requires attention of detail at farm level and careful sterilisation of equipment is necessary. Conception rate and the number of pigs born alive are both generally lower than with natural service.

The accurate timing of insemination is still probably the main obstacle to more widespread use of AI. The use of a boar is helpful, but in his absence back pressure on the sow can help to detect synthetic boar odour, aerosols are used to help in heat detection, and a piece of equipment introduced by Walls livestock, and known as the Walsmeta has also given good results.

MLC run demonstrations and provide instruction for on-farm insemination, which can be of tremendous assistance in improving conception rates and results.

Services Available

(1) Semen Delivery Service:

Semen is sent to the pig producer who makes his own arrangements for the insemination of his stock (by himself, his staff or his veterinary surgeon). Government legislation does not allow the pig producer to inseminate pigs outside his ownership. (The Artificial Insemination of Pigs (England & Wales) Regulations 1964.)

An efficient SDS depends on

(a) good transport facilities (rail, post, road).

(b) packages light, insulated, distinctively labelled and non-returnable.

(c) (i) supporting advisory service.
(ii) educational backing—courses, demonstrations, films, talks, literature.

(2) Inseminator Service (IS):

Trained staff inseminate pigs on request within a specific radius of the AI Centre. Reflects efficiency of centre and allows well-controlled trials to be conducted under field conditions.

Reasons for use of AI

(1) Livestock improvement:

Top 5 per cent of MLC performance tested boars (scoring 160 points for FC, GR and CQ) in AI Stud. Also boars from other testing programmes. Progeny testing carried out while standing at AI to check desirable characteristics are in fact inherited at nucleus, multiplier and commercial levels.

(2) MD herds and PHCA herds use AI with no known disease breakdowns.

(3) Quality control of semen:

Only semen of acceptable quality as assessed by bench tests used in AI. (No such check with natural service.)

(4) Boars screened for undesirable abnormalities:

All piglets from first 20 litters born to AI boars in IS are scrutinised for evidence of genetic abnormalities, e.g. congenital splay leg, inguinal hernia, atresia anus, pityriasis rosea, cryptorchidism, umbilical hernia, hermaphrodite, congenital tremor, genital malformation, etc.

(5) Batch farrowing facilities.

(6) Useful for emergencies, such as standstill orders during outbreaks of notifiable disease such as SVD.

PEDIGREE PIG SOCIETIES

Not all our breeding herds operate under the umbrella of the MLC or company breeding schemes. Pedigree herds have been improving purebred strains since before the end of the last century, and this led to the formation of the National Pig Breeders Association (NPBA). This association has kept herd books, and been responsible for show-ring activities for live pigs and carcase competitions as well as organising sales of breeding stock. It was also responsible for some of the first national recording schemes and progeny testing in this country. Many pedigree breeders have become involved with breeding companies and others are still active in the MLC scheme.

The British Landrace Pig Society was formed in 1953, after the importation of that breed into the UK from Sweden. The society performs a similar function to the NPBA for the Landrace breed. Both of these organisations have been involved in the export of breeding stock throughout the world and have been active in the importation of new breeds to this country such as the Hampshire.

Chapter 5

HOUSING—Basic Requirements

BASIC REQUIREMENTS of the pig for growth or reproduction can be summarised under the following headings, and are generally considered as 'the environment'.

(1) Temperature.
(2) Ventilation and air movement.
(3) Space requirements.
(4) Relative humidity and light.
   Other considerations of vital importance at this stage include:
(a) Health, behaviour and animal welfare.
(b) Feeding and management systems.
(c) Stockman (access, comfort and operating conditions).
(d) Manure handling, storage and disposal.

THE ENVIRONMENT
Temperature
The in-pig sow
   Adult breeding sows can withstand a wide range of temperature as is instanced by many outdoor systems. The optimum range will be 12°C to 18°C for sows in yards or cubicles, while sows confined in stalls may need higher temperatures up to 21°C, but insulated floors or good deep bedding will often extend the range at the lower end of the scale.

The Sow and Litter
   There is an immediate conflict when we consider the basic requirements for the sow and litter, as the sow's needs whilst suckling are very similar to those during pregnancy—preferably between 15°C to 18°C—but the litter's requirements are quite different and vary widely from the new-born pig to the weaner.
   Inside the uterus the temperature is about 39°C to 40°C, so that at first the young pigs must be kept very warm, 26°C to 29°C for the first 48 hours from birth. Very low temperatures cause chilling from which many pigs never recover, and partial recovery often leads to a slowing down of movement and reaction which predisposes them to subsequent

crushing or overlying. These temperatures are most easily maintained by a well-designed and insulated house with an ambient temperature of about 15°C to 18°C, but supplementary space heating may be needed on occasions.

The local temperature for the new-born litter is best achieved by radiant heat such as infra-red lamps or gas heaters, or underfloor heating. A pair of 'spot light' infra-red heaters can help by attracting the pigs away from the sow, so reducing crushing.

After a few days one of the lamps can be removed or raised, and then the covered creep should provide a steady heat of 21°C to 24°C until three weeks of age. From then the temperature should reduce progressively to about 18°C to 21°C, at weaning.

The new-born piglet has very poorly-developed control of body heat and great care must be taken to avoid draughts at floor level, which will greatly reduce the effective temperature of their lying area.

The Weaner

Commercial experience is now becoming available on temperature and humidity requirements for the very early-weaned pig, which may be five to seven days or up to 18 days at weaning.

Work in Belgium by Dr Van der Hyde indicates a temperature of 26·7°C for the early-weaned pig in the tiered cages. This is a good guide, and agrees with the findings of workers in early weaning in tiered cages in the UK. A constant figure is essential, with total absence of floor draughts and control of relative humidity is vital to help in the control of pathogenic organisms. A relative humidity of about 45 to 50 per cent is recommended.

Pigs weaned into flat deck cages require a steady temperature of about 21°C to 24°C and very early-weaned pigs that have been in tiered cages can be subjected to this temperature figure by the time they have been weaned two or three weeks.

Fattening Pigs

There is a wide range of tolerance, according to research work, which varies from 4·4°C up to 24°C. The factors affecting the pig's comfort and performance include air movement, particularly draughts at pig level, and the number of pigs per pen. Quite obviously, a group of fattening pigs will be able to huddle together to increase their body temperature. The provision of straw bedding and insulated floors will also help to increase the temperature tolerance at the lower end of the scale. The optimum temperature is probably in the range 20°C and 23°C at pig level, which is very rarely achieved in commercial practice. In this range the pig will be at its most efficient as a converter of food into liveweight gain.

Ventilation and Air Movement—Summary

The In-pig Sow

Under semi-intensive conditions, ventilation rates are based on natural methods, but with complete elimination of floor draughts.

Sows confined in sow stalls will require an air movement, especially in summer, of about 350m³ per hour with a reduction in winter to one-tenth of this rate. This will almost certainly mean the use of mechanical ventilation equipment.

Sow and Litter

The variation between the requirements of the sow and those of the litter is as great as the difference between summer and winter conditions.

Also, in the UK, relatively small geographical distances give rise to dramatic changes in climate, so local topography and climatic conditions should be considered when planning ventilation.

Practical observation and experience have been used in constructing the following table, assuming an outside winter temperature of 4·4°C.

TABLE 11. Ventilation Rates for Breeding Sows

	Summer m³/hour	Winter m³/hour
Sows in stalls	300–350	30–35
Sows and litters in farrowing crates	400–500	40–45

The aim of ventilation in summer is to limit the temperature rise inside the house, and summer ventilation rates are calculated to set a temperature limit of 1·5°C to 3·3°C above the outside average temperature, as an acceptable maximum in the house.

The varying requirements for ventilation of livestock houses can be worked out in a series of calculations. A worked example of this can be found in Farm Electric Handbook No 10, *Controlled Environment*, produced by the Electricity Council.

The Early-weaned Pig

A great deal of precision is needed to control ventilation rates and to keep a steady temperature with a variation of only 0·55°C either way. Thermostatically-controlled fans are set to provide between six and eight air changes per hour. Fresh air coming into the house will be pre-heated before being drawn into the house through baffled inlets.

Grower and Fattening Pig

Satisfactory ventilation for the fattening pig can be achieved by good design of semi-intensive buildings, using adjustable flaps and inlets, and the heat given off by the animals creates convection currents, giving ventilation by 'stack' effect. The 'Suffolk' house and the 'Trobridge' are good examples of natural ventilation.

Fattening pigs in enclosed buildings have more specific demands and practical recommendations are given as follows:

TABLE 12. Ventilation Rates for the Fattening Pig

Liveweight (kg)	Summer m³/hour	Winter m³/hour
30–90	1·8 to 2·0	0·18 to 0·20

Space Requirements—Summary

The In-pig Sow

These will vary according to housing systems, but for yard accommodation each sow needs 1·3–1·8m² lying area, a scraped dunging area of a similar size and about 0·92m² for feeding. With access passages a total of between 3·6m² and 5·4m² per sow is needed.

Details of space requirements for other systems will be found under the appropriate headings in a later section on housing.

The Sow and Litter

Farrowing crates:
  Up to 3 weeks: 2·7 × 1·6m.
  With forward creep: 3·05 × 1·6m.
  Up to 5 or 6 weeks: 3·05 × 1·8m minimum.
Rearing pens:
  Solari type: 5·4 × 1·5m or with 0·9m rear-access
    passage: 5·1 × 1·5m.
  Creep area: 0·9 × 1·5m.
  Combined farrowing
    and rearing: 3·05 × 3·05m minimum.
  Creep area: 3·05 × 0·9m.
Group suckling pens: 5·5 to 7·3m² per sow and litter.
                              1·1 to 1·38m² creep area per litter group.

The Early-weaned Pig

Flat deck cage for 12 pigs from 5·4kg to 20kg: 1·2 × 2·4m.

The Fattener

Requirements will naturally vary according to the size and weight of the pig, but the following table can be drawn up as a guide.

These figures are for general guidance only, and will vary according to solid or slatted floors and to ventilation, bedding, house design and layout.

Reference should be made to the Codes of Recommendations for the Welfare of Livestock—Code No 2, Pigs.

TABLE 13. Space Requirements for Growing and Fattening Pigs

Type	Weight (kg)	Lying Area (sq metres)	Dunging Area (sq metres)
Weaner	20	0·15	0·08
	40	0·25	0·10
Pork	60	0·35	0·12
Cutter	70	0·40	0·14
Bacon	90	0·46	0·16
Heavy	110	0·60	0·20

Light

Light is not thought to be of any special importance in pig production, but there is little factual evidence on this point.

Where the sow is concerned, she does not appear to be affected by daylight length as do some other breeding animals, though it has been suggested that natural daylight may be an important factor in the breeding cycle patterns of sows and gilts confined in stalls, so daylight should be provided wherever possible. There is no clear evidence on light requirements for the sow and litter, and natural daylight conditions will need to be supplemented by artificial lighting for observation and inspection.

When windowless houses are used for farrowing and rearing, careful positioning of lighting is needed, although outside normal working hours infra-red lights and pilot lights often give sufficient light for routine inspection.

Relative Humidity

Pigs are comfortable in humidities above 50 per cent, but a combination of low temperature and high humidity should be avoided as cold damp conditions lead to extreme discomfort and poor performance. Relative humidity above 75 per cent to 80 per cent may cause deterioration to the building and lead to 'sweat house' conditions.

The Boar

The basic requirements of the adult boar are similar to those of other adult breeding stock in terms of environment. As the boar is usually housed individually, special care is needed to maintain standards. Welfare recommendations suggest that $7m^2$ should be allowed for living area, and at least $9·3m^2$ where living and service areas are combined. The boar pen should be sub-divided into sleeping and dunging areas, and there should be easy access to the service pen.

VENTILATION SYSTEMS

Ventilation requirements were detailed for the various classes of livestock in the previous section. A brief guide to systems is given with the aid of a few diagrams. Specific requirements can only be arrived at after careful calculation of the cubic capacity of the house, insulation values, temperatures and the number and weight of pigs to be housed.

Figures 6, 7 and 8 are, of necessity, over-simplified, as recent knowledge from experimental work carried out at the National Institute of Agricultural Engineering has shown. Air flow patterns and air distribution within a building has been determined at the NIAE by use of bubble equipment and photography. It is generally accepted that air

Natural Ventilation

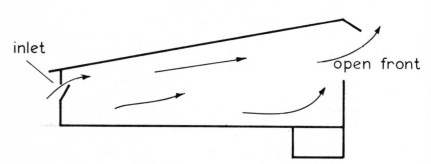

FIG. 4. *Natural ventilation in monopitch housing.*

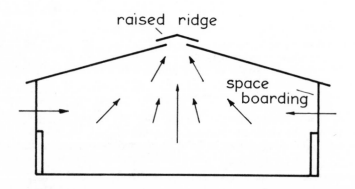

FIG. 5. *Natural ventilation in Suffolk-type house showing 'stack' effect.*

Mechanised Ventilation

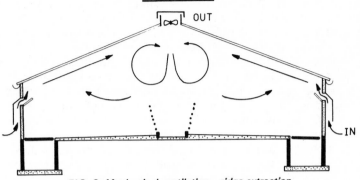

FIG. 6. *Mechanical ventilation—ridge extraction*

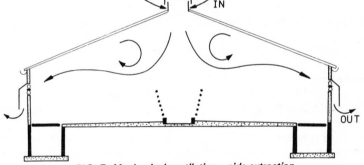

FIG. 7. *Mechanical ventilation—side extraction.*

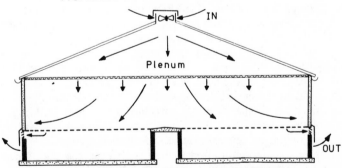

FIG. 8. *Mechanical ventilation—pressurised system.*

distribution within a pig building is controlled by a number of factors, including the number and position of inlets and fans, as well as convection currents arising from heat generated by the pigs in the building and the temperature of the incoming air.

NIAE work has highlighted the importance in ventilation systems of the air inlets. It appears that it is important, especially with cool incoming air, to restrict the inlet area but at the same time to keep up the inlet velocity. Obstructions such as pen divisions were shown to have a significant effect on air flow and distribution within a building, and quite small obstructions such as protruding purlins—about 25mm in depth—could change air flow patterns and air circulation.

In practice some form of mechanised control of air inlets would be advantageous, similar to the type of control used for greenhouse ventilation systems. Alternatively, ducted systems have an important role to play, in which a series of holes acting as air inlets can be positioned along the length of the duct. These inlets direct jets of fresh air into the building with sufficient velocity to provide efficient air distribution down the length of the house. Ducts can be constructed of various materials including polythene, hardboards, or plastics (see fig. 9).

The NIAE work also demonstrated that it is perhaps misleading to think in traditional terms of summer and winter ventilation rates as giving respectively cold (minimum) and hot (maximum) ventilation rates. It is now apparent that airflow patterns begin to change, and may even reverse, when the outside ambient temperature is about 14°C. This reversal could take place on over 30 per cent of days during the summer period from May to September. In practice, when outside temperatures are above 15°C, a strong air flow moves along the ceiling line from wall-mounted inlets with a secondary air flow at pig level. However, if the temperature drops below 13°C the incoming air follows a quite different path, forming a rotary pattern in the opposite direction.

The practical implications of this type of work are now being applied and this is especially important as the cost of energy in either pig food or artificial heating has increased substantially over the past few years.

In house layout more consideration must be given to the siting, design and construction of air inlets, as well as the positioning of fans. Greater care must be taken of the control equipment, and of the maintenance and care of delicate sensing devices such as thermostats and thermistors.

Careful siting of the pighouse in relation to other buildings and topographical features can also be a critical factor in the successful design and operation of a mechanical ventilation system.

The object of any ventilation system is to keep the pig as near as possible to its lower critical temperature. If this temperature is not maintained, the pig will need to eat extra food in order to keep up its body temperature. This amount of food can now be quantified, and the table on page 65 illustrates the amount of extra food required each day for each degree Centigrade below the lower critical temperature.

For instance, an 80kg pig will require 20 extra grams of food per day for every 1°C drop below lower critical temperature. In a large commercial fattening house with 400 pigs, this can add a considerable extra amount to the food cost.

It should be added that critical temperature will also be affected by the number of pigs in the pen group, the floor surfaces and the amount of insulation, as well as the amount of bedding that might be used.

Extra Food Required Per Day Per °C Below Critical Temperature

Wt. of pig (kg)	Lower Critical Temp. (°C)	Grams of Food per pig
10	25	6
20	22	10
40	17	16
60	14	18
80	12	20
100	10	20

Control of the pig's environment has now become more of a practical science as the basic principles are becoming defined, better understood, and put into practice with improved electronic controls and equipment, as well as improved design and layout of specialist pig housing.

MATERIALS

Materials used in prefabrication include a wide range of hardboards as well as the traditional soft-woods. Asbestos, plastics, polyurethanes and steel are also widely used and the agricultural sector is getting a useful 'spin-off' from industrial building sources. Bricks and concrete blocks are still the first choice for walling and basework. Many of

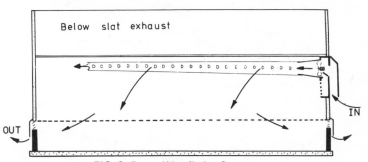

FIG. 9. *Ducted Ventilation System*

these materials are available for the farmer who prefers to build his own house on more traditional lines.

Essentially, pig housing should provide correct environmental conditions for the class of pig housed as economically as possible. To prevent heat escaping, a high standard of insulation is required as most heat losses are through the roof, walls, floors and windows—in that

C

order. A correctly insulated building will keep warm in winter and cool in summer and this is a first essential in pig housing.

The insulation value of a material is measured by a term known as the 'U' value, and the lower the 'U' value the better the insulating material. 'U' value can be defined as the amount of heat in BTUs that is transmitted through one square metre of the construction from the air inside to the air outside when there is 0·55°F difference in temperature between inside and outside.

The metric equivalent now currently in use is the number of watts of energy which pass through a square metre of the building when the temperature difference between one side and the other is 1°C. This can be expressed as follows:

1 Btu/ft²/h/°F = 5·67826 W/M²/°C.

Targets for insulation values should now be as follows:

Floors	1·14 Watts/m²/°C.
Walls	0·7 Watts/m²/°C.
Ceiling and Roof	0·6 Watts/m²/°C.

There are many ways of achieving this target in house construction with a variety of new materials now available. The efficiency of the insulation material will be rapidly reduced if it becomes wet, so a vapour seal is essential. For example, where a glass fibre quilt is used it should be sealed in a plastic bag. An expanded plastic sheet such as fibre-board or polyurethane should have a bonded hygienic plastic surface.

Two forms of roof insulation are illustrated below:

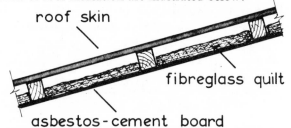

FIG. 10. *Roof insulation—mineral wool quilt with plastic lining.*

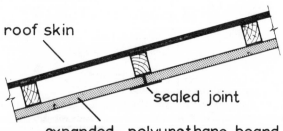

FIG. 11. *Roof insulation using polyurethane board.*

WALL INSULATION

This can be achieved in several ways with prefabricated construction using polystyrenes and internal linings or by lightweight insulated blocks.

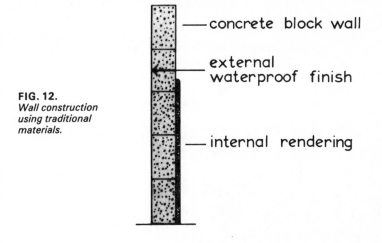

— concrete block wall

— external waterproof finish

— internal rendering

FIG. 12.
Wall construction using traditional materials.

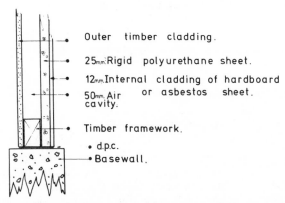

Outer timber cladding.

25mm.Rigid polyurethane sheet.

12mm.Internal cladding of hardboard or asbestos sheet.

50mm.Air cavity.

Timber framework.

d.p.c.

Basewall.

FIG. 13. *Wall construction using prefabricated materials. 'U' value = 0·58*

FLOOR INSULATION

A wide variety of methods can be used, but in practice I find the best is to use a 'No fines' aggregate to a depth of 76–102mm. This then gives a good 'key' for the final screed which is less likely to break up than when placed on a polystyrene or polyurethane board.

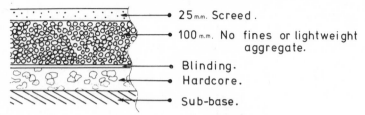

- 25 m.m. Screed.
- 100 m.m. No fines or lightweight aggregate.
- Blinding.
- Hardcore.
- Sub-base.

FIG. 14. *Floor insulation using aggregates.*

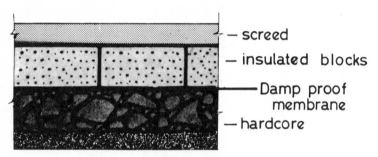

— screed

— insulated blocks

——Damp proof membrane

— hardcore

FIG. 15. *Floor insulation using hollow blocks.*

WINDOWS

Many prefabricated houses will be windowless. Where windows are fitted—such as in sow-stall housing—they must be double glazed and well fitted.

PREFABRICATION AND STANDARDISATION

With the increasing specialisation in pig production, there is a trend towards the use of prefabricated type of construction for many pig-houses. These buildings are made under factory conditions by firms who specialise in intensive livestock housing or by manufacturers who are already engaged in fabricating industrial joinery lines such as schools, offices and domestic housing. These pighouses are delivered on site and erected on a prepared base in a matter of a few days. Internal fittings and fixtures are then completed under cover without interference from the weather.

There were a large number of firms and options in the market, but the competition in this sector of the industry has been fierce and only a handful of firms remain in business. These firms reach a high standard of workmanship and design and are prepared to carry out a package deal that includes planning permission, site works, house bases, as well as erection and completion of all superstructure.

Fortunately the pig industry is arriving at a stage where housing and management requirements have been developed and refined so that advantage can be taken of prefabrication with factories tooled up to streamline production. This rationalisation of design will mean that less time is spent on 'one-off' buildings and that standard plans, fitting and components can be used, cheaper and better construction can be achieved in the factory and in some cases expansion plans can be better accommodated.

MANURE: SOLID OR LIQUID

A basic decision will have to be taken about manure handling and storage policies. On most farms this decision will largely determine housing and management policies. In cereal-growing areas where straw is available, straw bedding, solid floors and mechanised scrapers will be the usual choice. The straw will make housing conditions less critical and pigs will create their own micro-climate with the straw as bedding. As a result, management is usually easier, but there are handling and storage charges to consider. Mechanisation of scraping will reduce labour cost and some farms prefer solid manure for use in arable rotations.

TABLE 14. Volume of Waste Produced

Animal	Live wt (kg)	Litres/Day	Cu. Metres per Week
Piglet	15	1·04	·007
Weaner	30	1·9	·013
Porker	70	4·4	·031
Baconer	90	5·8	·041
Dry Sow	125	4·03	·028
Sow and litter	170	14·9	·104
Boar	160	4·9	·034

After Robertson.

Well-designed slurry systems are certainly labour saving, and partially slatted floors are a feature of many intensive units. Problems arise with disposal when the unit is sited on a farm with limited acreage. Smell, nuisance and pollution of water courses must be avoided and a large research effort is now being directed towards finding a solution for the disposal of all farm effluents.

These amounts are guides only and will vary according to method of housing and access to water. Nipple drinkers in a feeding house may add 10 per cent to the total slurry produced. Water used for washing and swilling out must be added to the above quantities.

Figures for consideration in slurry and manure spreading are as follows:

TABLE 15. Available Nutrients in Pig Manure

(a) Undiluted Slurry

N Kg/m^3	P_2O_5 Kg/m^3	K_2O Kg/m^3
4·0	2·0	2·7

At February 1981 fertiliser prices, one cubic metre of pig slurry (10 per cent. dry matter) is valued at £2·52.

(b) 10 Tonnes of Fresh Straw Manure

N (kg)	P_2O_5 (kg)	K_2O (kg)
15	40	25

At February 1981 fertiliser prices, 10 tonnes of solid pig manure is valued at £23·20.

Slurry Spreading

Maximum yearly figures for organic irrigation by pipeline or tanker spreading are about 150–170m^3/ha. This will depend on type of land, season of year and cropping programme, but this application rate is a useful guide, with a maximum of 55m^3/ha at any one time.

Manure Spreading

Solid farmyard manure can usually be spread at about 37·5 tonnes per hectare. On exceptionally dry light land this figure could be doubled, where heavy land is subject to poaching and wheelmarks then half the quantity only. Straw usage on a farm using entirely straw for bedding will be in the region of 0·75 to 1·3 tonnes per sow and progeny per year. Thus a 100-sow unit feeding pigs for bacon production would use 75 tonnes to 130 tonnes of straw, depending on particular details of housing and generosity of the stockman.

SLURRY STORAGE

Below-ground tanks which are an integral part of the housing system usually have only a few weeks capacity, and these will be described in a later section under the various types of housing. Sluice-gate systems can be designed to flush liquids into a central, below-ground, collecting pit. An alternative uses above-ground circular storage tanks made of steel or vitreous enamel silo bases, or concrete storage tanks. Augers or pumps are then needed to lift the slurry from pit to storage area. On some farms and on suitable land large lagoons have been constructed with earth bank retaining walls and clay bases. These normally have a limited life and may sludge up after several years.

Tank Capacities

Reception Pits

Length (m)	Width (m)	Depth (m)	Capacity (m³)
3·0	3·0	2·4	23
15·2	3·0	2·4	115

Above-Ground Circular

Height (m)	Diameter (m)	Capacity (m³)
7·30	2·1	85
11·95	3·0	308
14·50	4·5	685
18·75	4·5	1158

SLURRY—A PROBLEM AREA

Where an intensive unit is an integral part of a grassland or arable farm the best solution is by a vacuum tanker operation or organic irrigation by pipeline—or a combination of these methods. Storage capacity can be increased by having collecting pits and central storage above or below ground. Where lagoons are used, slurry will be pumped from the buildings on a fairly regular basis—say weekly—to the storage lagoon.

Probably about 85 per cent of pig farmers will be able to manage slurry storage and handling by conventional methods. With the increasing cost of artificial fertilisers, pig slurry has become a valuable by-product that should be carefully utilised by spreading on the land.

There is, however, increasing pressure from Local Authorities, environmental interests and local residents on those pig farmers who are located on the edge of towns and villages, particularly in densely pig populated areas such as the Holderness area of North Humberside. In fact, in 1977, the Planning Department of Humberside County Council produced a consultative report on Intensive Livestock Units, drawing attention to the problems of livestock being reared under intensive housing conditions, with special reference to the deterioration of amenities associated with intensive pig units. The main grievance from local residents is about smells, particularly during spreading. Other complaints include noise from animals and machinery, and nuisance from insects and vermin.

These are some of the problems faced by the intensive pig unit, and a more general awareness of the environment and a demand for reduction in pollution has highlighted these problems. Since the early 1970s the Government, through the Agricultural Research Council, the Universities, MAFF, and ADAS, has been concentrating on these problem areas. Commercial organisations have also become involved in the application of research, as well as pioneering methods of treatment, handling, and storage of liquid manure.

CURRENT DEVELOPMENTS

Spreading

A number of spreaders have been developed which direct the slurry downwards when spreading, helping to minimise spray which causes most of the problems. An alternative method is to inject the slurry directly into the ground, which virtually eliminates smell and places the nutrients directly at root level. However, with the latter method the rate of operation is slowed down, a good deal of power is required, and this type of machinery can be difficult to operate on some soils and on difficult slopes and terrain.

Recently Newcastle University Department of Agricultural Engineering has been developing a dribble bar system which looks very promising and which has a good work rate, as well as preventing drift and spray.

Separation

Most of the difficulties in handling slurry are caused by fibre residues from the feed which come through into the slurry undigested, creating blockages in tankers, pipelines, and pumps.

Equipment has now been developed for the purpose of efficiently separating solids from the liquid portion. A number of methods are used, including vibrating screens, stationary screens with hydraulic or rotary presses, rotary screens, and belt separators.

The benefits of separation include some reduction in smells and the production of stackable, easily handled solids. The liquid is easily pumped, is free-flowing, and retains most of the nutrient value of the original slurry. Between 15–20 per cent of the slurry will be removed as solids so that storage area for liquids is increased by a similar amount, leaving that much extra storage area for liquids. In some areas there may be a sale for the separated solids after they have been composted for a few days, especially if they can be handled and attractively packed for garden and horticultural use.

The separated liquid is much easier to handle and pump, is less likely to block organic pipeline systems, and could be used with small-bore irrigation systems. Sampling is also much simplified in order to obtain a more accurate fertiliser plan for the farm.

For pig farms with slurry handling problems a separation technique seems to be a logical development. This will require a central reception pit into which slurry must be sluiced or pumped. Equipment available on the market appears to be well developed, robust, and there is a choice from several manufacturers. Moreover, separation of solids from liquids is an essential first step for any other treatment system that may be developed in the next few years.

Treatment Systems

An intensive effort has been put into finding treatment systems that can be operated practically at farm level.

Biological treatment methods based on human sewage systems have not really been effective, but development work continues on aerobic liquid treatment systems in which a variety of mechanical aeration systems are used for oxygenation of the wastes. Research has yet to provide all the parameters for simple farm systems from which treated slurry can be returned to the land.

Anaerobic biological systems are still the subject of research projects, and the development of a plant to operate under commercial farming conditions could provide methane gas as one of the final products. However, the control of all the factors affecting digestion and fermentation for an effective and simple system to be operated by farm staff has not yet been determined.

One complete treatment of current interest is based on a composting system in which the animal waste is mixed with straw in carefully controlled proportions. This treatment is known as the 'Arcub' process, and has been developed by the Department of Chemical Engineering at Birmingham University, with the backing of a grant from the Agricultural Research Council. The process is aerobic and there is virtually no smell, and the final product is a valuable horticultural compost for direct field application. In areas where farms have a good local supply of straw this could be a good commercial technique for treating and disposing of pig slurry.

Further work on complete treatment of pig slurry is being carried out at the National Institute of Agricultural Engineering. This is based on separation, high-rate filtration, sludge settlement, and a de-watering system developed there. The next stage in this research is the construction of a fattening house at the MAFF Experimental Farm at Terrington, using the NIAE techniques in an integral waste system.

Looking ahead, I believe that separation is the key to most future slurry developments on the intensive pig unit, especially if this is linked to a flushing and recirculation system. This should go a long way towards solving the problems of smell, storage, and handling, as well as helping to improve the environment within the pig house.

Chapter 6

HOUSING—Stock

Outdoor Housing

A SMALL minority of pig farmers will continue to house dry sows outdoors. This traditional approach is still valid where there is very cheap land which has no alternative use, or where outdoor sows are part of an arable break. Light, dry land is essential, otherwise excessive poaching leads to a situation where it becomes impossible to service the unit. Labour charges can be very high, especially if the system is operated all the year round. Fencing, pig movement and collection can also prove difficult. This is essentially a low-cost operation with possibly low output, although very successful out-door units modelled on the Roadnight system remain very profitable.

Housing can be made of curved corrugated sheets with one end boarded in, thus forming a draught-free, warm, snug pocket. A fairly generous amount of straw is used, and at farrowing a retaining board keeps the litter inside the shelter for a few days.

Wooden huts and runs have also been used successfully and are, in fact, an updated version of the traditional range house. A farrowing crate or frame is now incorporated which gives protection at birth. Heat and light can be provided by portable gas systems. These huts are frequently drawn up onto concrete bases during winter months.

Maintenance costs are high on these systems, and although mucking out is reduced, supervision can be difficult and uncomfortable. There is certainly an advantage in the health of the pig and robust weaners are often produced. However, even in our traditional outdoor areas the sow is moving indoors and the eclipse of our hardier coloured breeds is accelerating this trend.

Intensive Housing

Fully Covered Yards

The first move indoors was often into yards or cattle courts that provided basic shelter and deep bedding conditions. Groups of sows might number up to 30 or 40 in various stages of pregnancy, and a catch boar would be running with them. Feeding might be in a long trough with plenty of opportunity for bullying, with the result that the fat sows became fatter and the thin ones even thinner.

1. Batch of hybrid gilts hardening off in straw yards. *NDP photo*

2. Organic irrigation of pig effluent—the ideal solution where land is available.

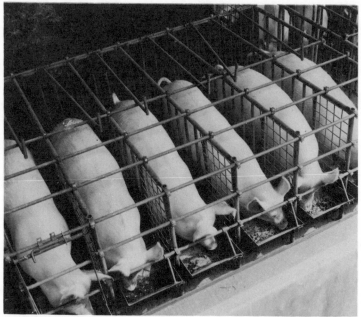

3. Sow yards showing sow feeders.

4. Sow yard showing groups of sows lying in the kennels.

FBC photo

5. Groups of sows in a cubicle house.

6. Sow yards with boar pens and service area adjacent.

7. General view of a large sow-stall house.   *NPD photo*

8. Sow-stall house with boar pens and service area at the end of the house.

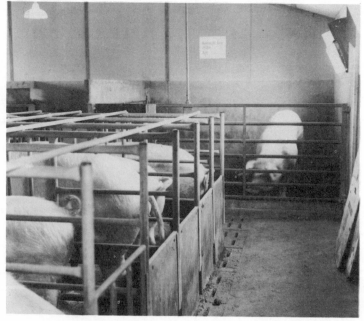

9. Close-up of individual sow-stall showing concrete slatted floor.

10. Tethered sows on solid floors showing back-to-back layout.

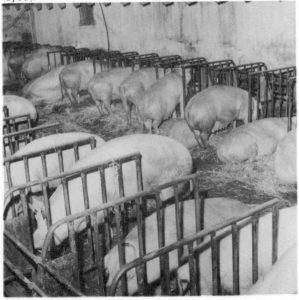

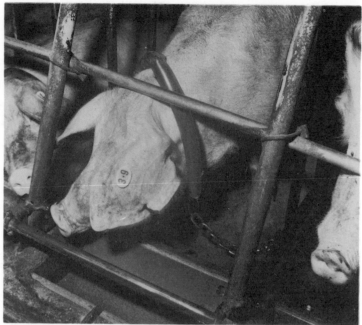

11. Close-up of neck tether on sow.

12. General view of maternity section in farrowing house. *NPD photo*

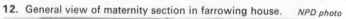

13. Close-up view of sow in farrowing crate on solid floor.

14. Sow and litter in partially slatted farrowing crate.

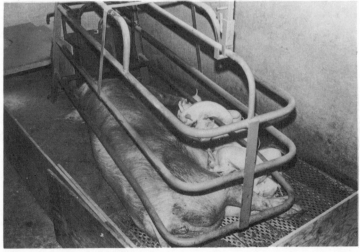

15. Flat deck cage in litter groups.

16. Flat deck cage house—general view.

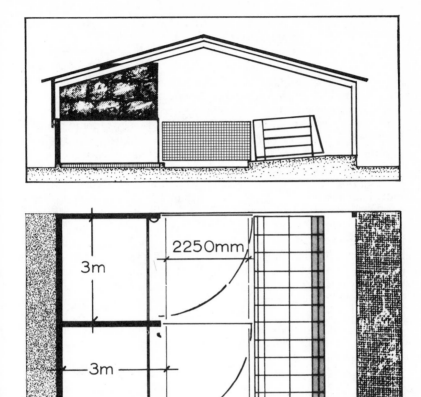

FIG. 16. *Fully-covered yards for groups of sows with individual feeders.*

From this situation some basic principles were evolved. Individual feeding is essential and feeders must be provided. These can be shared by several groups, but the wisdom of saving on capital cost at the expense of labour and waiting time should be questioned. Group size must be brought down to a figure of about six to ten sows at the same stage of pregnancy in each yard. Batch weaning and batch farrowing fit into the housing pattern, but it required a herd of about 150 sows to provide this sort of group on a regular basis. Smaller herds must consider smaller groups which will put up the costs.

Whilst deep bedding can be used, this is costly in terms of both space and bedding materials. If an insulated kennel area can be provided, the space required for sleeping can be reduced to $1 \cdot 1$ to $1 \cdot 38 m^2$ per sow.

The kennel area can provide local insulation and also carry the baled straw or litter for bedding down.

A general-purpose clear-span building gives the best cover for this sort of housing system and retains some flexibility for other farm purposes. Straw storage can be obtained and room allowed for a tractor-scraping cleaning operation. Sows can be shut in the feeders or closed in by the gates into the kennels.

A scraping passage of about 0·82 to 0·92m is required and cleaning out takes place two or three times each week. Internal walls can be of 152mm blockwork and the front of the kennel half closed by a return wall on exposed sites. An open front gives better observation and cleaner lying conditions but some protection may be needed in winter. Individual feeders should be provided in banks of the appropriate number and preferably fixed to the ground. A number of different types are manufactured and points to look for centre around trough and rear gate design, with a generally robust construction as they come in for considerable punishment from adult breeding stock. Water should be provided by an automatic bowl sited just on the edge of the kennel area so that any spillage is caught in the scraping area. A straw board across the entrance to the kennel will prevent too much straw being pulled out of the lying area by the sows.

Boar housing will be dealt with under a separate heading, but newly weaned sows should be housed within sight and sound of the boar in a special service area.

Deep straw yards can still be used providing plenty of straw is available. An overall allowance of 4·6–5·4m^2 per sow is essential. Floor feeding with nuts or cobs will be the best choice of feeding under these conditions and periodic cleaning out will be carried out with tractor and foreloader. Group size should be limited as in the more conventional yarded system described earlier.

A slightly cheaper variation on the covered yard is a simple mono-pitch building which covers the kennel area only. Scraping yards and feeders are not under cover, which probably gives a more liquid manure and less agreeable working conditions for the stockmen.

The principles, however, remain: of small groups, well-bedded and insulated lying areas, and individual feeding with good weaning and service facilities.

Sow Cubicles

This system of dry sow housing is a compromise between the entire freedom of the yard system and the confinement of the sow stall or tether. The design is based upon the use of the individual lying area under a kennel roof, giving a warm dry draught-free lie. Sows have access to a scraped dunging passage where the drinker is placed. Use

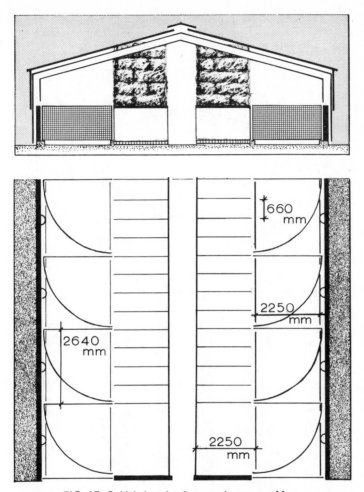

FIG. 17. *Cubicle housing for sows in groups of four.*

is again made of the general-purpose building and some straw storage can be obtained. Mechanical cleaning out is possible, but sow numbers should be no more than three to five in a group. Observation can be difficult unless service and inspection passages are provided, and like most compromises the worst of both worlds can be found rather than the best. This can lead to bullying and a tendency for several sows to attempt to get into the same cubicle at the same time, with damage to the sow at the vulva, legs and udder.

Cubicles, however, lend themselves to a do-it-yourself approach which appeals to some pig farmers, but dimensions and width of cubicles and passages are critical. Straw bedding, and materials such as sawdust and shavings, can be used for bedding down and the system

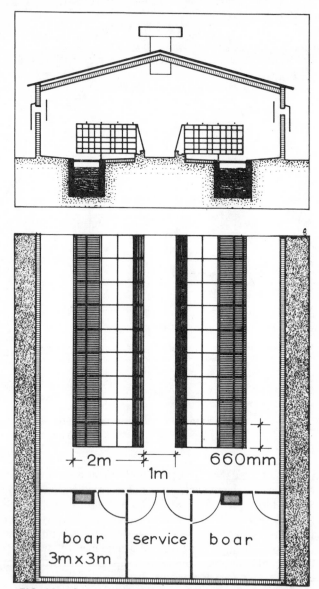

FIG. 18. *A 2-row sow-stall house with partially-slatted floors.*

is best suited to solid floors. Boar housing and service facilities are again critical.

Sow Stalls

The system of housing the individual sow in confinement throughout pregnancy was introduced into this country from Scandinavia. Most of the pioneer work took place in Scotland and was encouraged by a close liaison and partnership between the North of Scotland Farm Buildings Institute and local farmers. Sow stalls are now used widely in large-scale commercial pig production and the advantages are well known. Individual treatment of the sow is possible and feeding methods can be followed precisely. Bullying and fighting, which is a feature of group housing systems, is now eliminated. Very large economies on labour can be made and working conditions are improved for stockmen. Careful design of the detail is very important, especially if partially slatted floors are used. An insulated bed is essential and an open rear gate design should eliminate any chafing or rubbing at the back of the sow.

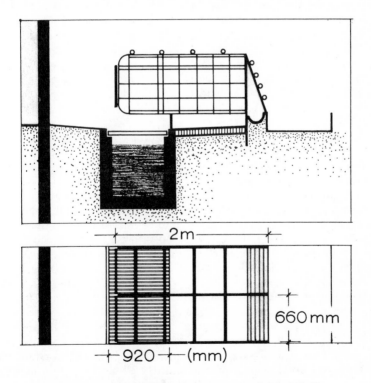

FIG. 19. *Tubular sow-stall showing trough and floor details.*

Individual feeding is best catered for by a half-round salt-glazed trough, and after many attempts with a variety of watering systems I prefer a small quantity of water to be available in the bottom of the trought at all times. This is achieved by a valve device placed at one end of the trough run which releases water as required. Level troughs are essential for this and I prefer trough dividers carried on the sow stall division to stop poaching at feeding times. Overall dimensions are usually $2m \times 635mm$ and the open stall frames provide plenty of contact between sows. Preferably sows will face each other if in two rows, but this does not appear to be critical.

As sows are confined at all times, environmental requirements are critical. Insulation values must be designed to maintain the recommended temperature of $16°C$–$20°C$. I feel that many sow stall houses are much too cold and this leads to management problems. Draught-free conditions are essential, especially the elimination of floor draughts where open rear gates are used. Without doubt a sow stall system with partially slatted floors is most economical on labour, but slat design is critical. Several materials have been tried out but a well-finished concrete panel is the best answer. In my experience the gaps between slats should be no more than 13mm and should run parallel with the sow stall. Edges of new slats should be trimmed with a carborundum stone so that with wear and tear the gap will be a nominal 20mm with a solid portion of 51mm to 64mm. Solid floor sow stalls are acceptable but give dirtier sows and although bedding materials such as straw, sawdust and wood shavings can be used there is a high labour requirement for daily cleaning out.

Sow stalls are now finally established in the UK pig industry and are probably the best method of housing pregnant sows. Attention to detail of floor design is very important and also to ventilation to prevent excessive heat loss.

One other major step forward is the provision of some form of automatic or semi-automatic feeding. I prefer the semi-automatic type based on a strong box container fixed in front of each individual stall. Food is released for a whole row by operating a handle which allows food to be discharged from the base of each sow feeder simultaneously. In this way, even a large house with 300 or 400 sows can be fed in a few minutes. This reduces stress on both sows and stockmen and allows better and more accurate distribution of food. The manual feeders are then refilled according to requirements as the sows are feeding, which probably gives 25–30 minutes in which to do the job carefully.

Fully automatic systems can be used but are more expensive and require a good deal of adjustment on a daily basis. The semi-automatic system gives good control without entirely eliminating stockmanship and at a cost at current prices (1978) of about £10–£12 per sow place.

Tethers

The more likely choice where a solid floor system has to be used is a tethered sow stall. The metal work is shorter as the sow is confined by a neck girth tether, and so it is easier for the stockman to operate at the back-end. Careful attention is again needed to design detail. Feeding and watering arrangement can be the same as for the stalled sow, with an insulated lying area, giving a back step from which dung can be scraped easily. Neck-tether design has improved recently, and rubbing and chafing are prevented by the use of rubber or polythene covering the tether chain, which is fixed to a locating point on the floor or on the stall frame. Some sows, especially the lop-eared types, are capable of slipping the neck tether and a body-girth tether has been adopted from the Continent. This plastic or polythene 'belt' holds the sow firmly, and is usually fixed on the stall frame. Adjustments may be

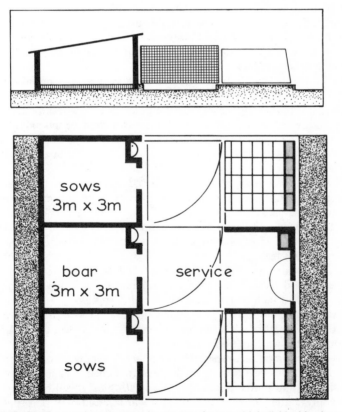

FIG. 20. *Boar and service area for groups of sows with individual feeders.*

necessary from time to time as the sow increases in body size during pregnancy.

Tether systems which use bedding are a little less demanding of the environmental conditions than a slatted sow stall system, and they are lower in capital cost and appeal to the farmer prepared to do the conversion himself. Heads can be placed to the outer wall to give a central cleaning-out passage, but in some very narrow buildings, without space for outer feed passages, it is necessary to walk up the side of the sow to feed her.

THE BOAR AND SERVICE AREAS

The boar has long been the neglected animal in most of our breeding herds. Service often went unrecorded and undetected, especially when the boar ran with a group of sows. However, the introduction of sow stalls and tethers has changed all that.

Individual housing has highlighted the importance of effective boar service, and a trend towards earlier weaning has added emphasis to this. As the boar is housed individually, temperature becomes important as well as a draught-proof sleeping area, good feeding and watering arrangements.

A well-bedded pen adjacent to the service area is essential with at least 7·2m² or 9·3m² if the boar pen is combined with the service area. I prefer a separate service pen as the boar usually works better away from his own quarters. A work routine can then be planned which allows the stockman to bring sows to the service pen without interference from the boar. Safety is an important factor in boar pen design and layout.

Newly-weaned sows should be housed next to the boar's living quarters as sight, sound and smell will encourage the newly-weaned sow to come on heat. An open pen front or open gate will help the boar see the sows, but pen divisions and gates need to be fairly robust and frames with 25mm square sections will do this job nicely. A square service pen, at least 3m × 3m, without projections, and with a non-slip floor make ideal operating conditions for boar and stockman. A tamped, wooden float finish on the concrete should give the non-slip surface, but an inch or two of sawdust will also help.

An insulated floor area is required in the boar's sleeping area and where he is in an outside situation adjacent to sow yards, then a kennel provides extra warmth and comfort.

Special treatment is needed for the boar, as surveys show that many extremely expensive and well-bred boars are culled because of arthritic and rheumatoid joints. Supplementary heating may well be justified in very cold weather to provide that extra warmth and may well speed up his performance in extreme conditions.

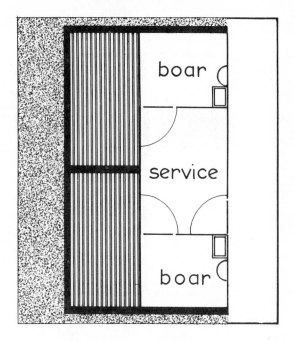

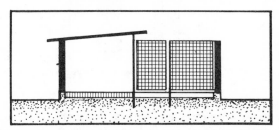

FIG. 21. *Boar pens and service area as used at the NAC Pig Unit.*

Service Areas

In sow stall and tether houses one particular portion, preferably at one end, can be allocated to newly-weaned sows with the boars only a few feet away. In sow stall houses it is relatively easy to move sows to the service pen, but in tether houses it may be better to work the boar behind the tethered sow.

Floor profiles and passageways may make this difficult and in some tethered systems sows are grouped in a separate service area, held there for three to four weeks, and confirmed in pig before being tethered in the main house. Some layouts are suggested in the drawings and illustrations.

In sow stall and tether houses I prefer to define one specific area as a

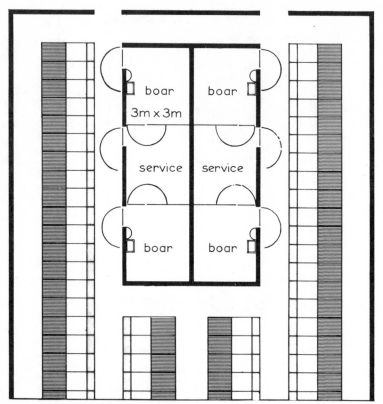

FIG. 22. *Layout of boar pens and service areas in large sow-stall or tether house.*

place to house newly-weaned sows. This is illustrated in Fig 22, where newly-weaned sows are housed opposite the boar pens. Front opening sow stalls can be an advantage in this situation. As an alternative in a four-row stall house, it is possible to house the boars on the outside of the building allowing the two central rows of stalls to run through the centre for housing the newly-weaned sows.

Good lighting will help observation, and a non-slip surface on the floor of the service area is essential if this system is going to work well.

Individual housing of the newly-weaned sow would be ideal but where this cannot be done individual feeders should be provided. Gilts should be housed in a group system and served and confirmed in pig before being placed in stalls or tethers. Some units will carry gilts until farrowing on a group system and this appears to work quite well. If possible, service areas should be under cover, although this will push up the capital cost.

Better working and housing conditions for the boar and attention to the housing of newly-weaned sows are the areas which most need improvement in our breeding herds at the present time. This is the key area, and sow productivity will improve as attention is directed towards boar housing and service areas.

HOUSING OF GILTS

Maiden gilts, whether bought in or home bred, can present problems as they require special facilities. They do not settle well into stall or tether systems and the best plan is to provide yards in an area which includes some boar housing. This can often be incorporated with straw and litter storage in a general-purpose building. Yards with individual feeders are ideal, but floor feeding with large nuts would be acceptable. Fresh air and exercise are important at this hardening-off stage, and they should be housed partially on concrete to firm up legs and action. Boars should not at this stage run in the yards with the gilts, but should be housed adjacent ready for use.

FARROWING AND REARING

The farrowing crate is now widely used to provide piglet protection at birth. This crate is an essential piece of equipment and will help to reduce that alarming pre-weaning mortality which is often between 10 per cent and 20 per cent. A well-laid-out crate system provides better working conditions for staff and is the focal point of most commercial pig units. Crate houses are best subdivided into a number of sections with six to ten crates in each room. The exact number will depend on herd size, and smaller numbers give better management and health control. Ideally, room size should be matched to weekly farrowing requirements so an 'all in—all out' policy can be followed.

Environmental conditions are again critical and these smaller rooms are easier to keep warm and ventilate. Local heating for newly-born pigs is provided by artificial heating and insulated floors are essential. Optimum layout would be for the two rows of crates to face each other to give a central feed passage and outer service passages, but the reverse is quite acceptable. In narrow buildings heads can be placed against the outside wall, but, whilst saving space, this means that the stockman has to walk up the side of each sow to feed her.

There are a number of crate designs on the market and the most popular form of construction is of tubular steel. This gives a robust framework with good all-round visibility. Trough and watering details are points to watch, and I prefer the type of crate which carries the rear legs well clear of the back end of the sow. If sow size varies a good deal and a narrow crate is selected, than an adjustable bottom rail can be an advantage.

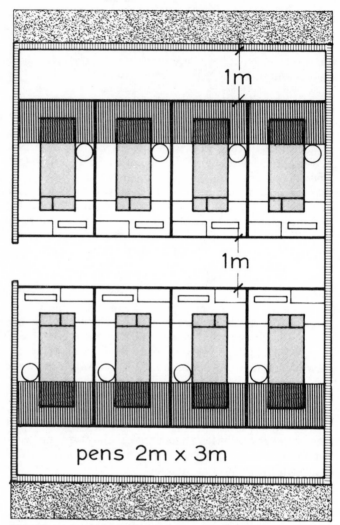

FIG. 23. *Layout of maternity farrowing crates with forward creep area.*

Floor Design and Layout

Whilst solid floors are widely used, there has been a move towards the use of the partially slatted and fully slatted floor; these labour-saving layouts keep sows and litters cleaner whilst reducing the daily cleaning out by hand.

A number of materials have been used including timber, weldmesh and concrete slats. Expanded metal sheets have been widely adopted and more recently perforated punched metal panels have been introduced, and both these materials are better galvanised for longer life. Expanded metal has not been very successful, with injuries to piglets' feet and the sows' teats and vulva. Investigational work is being carried out in Scotland by the Veterinary Investigation Service and the Scottish Farm Buildings Investigation unit at Aberdeen on a number of materials.

A good floor should satisfy the following requirements:

(a) provide a non-slip, non-abrasive surface for sow and litter;
(b) provide an acceptable level of cleanliness and should be easy to clean;
(c) should be durable, hard wearing and with reasonable life—say four to five years at least;
(d) should be reasonable in cost and easy to fit and replace.

The material most likely to meet these requirements at the present time is the galvanised punched metal panel, but standards vary widely between various manufacturers and great care is needed in selection and examination of the actual panels used.

Other materials are under test and investigation at both the NAC and the Scottish FBIU at Aberdeen. Expanded plastics, polythene and plastic-coated metals are some of the materials under examination at present, and I feel that cost should not be a major factor in the final selection of the materials used for this vital area of flooring.

Partially Slatted

Where partially slatted floors are used, they should be fitted across the whole width of the pen and extend about one metre from the tailgate of the crate so that the rear feet of the sow are on the partially slatted area. The dung channel will then run the length into an outside underground storage tank. Occasionally slurry can be pumped directly from below the slats, but in each case a fairly generous amount of water should be placed in the dung channel before the sows are moved in as this will help with slurry removal.

Fully Slatted

Fully slatted floors have been introduced from Europe but add extra capital cost and can give problems of sow comfort and in removing slurry from below slat. Sows and litters keep very clean, and labour in cleaning out is reduced. Where fully slatted floors are used I recommend that a solid floor front creep should be fitted which provides heat, light and comfort for the litter as well as giving an area for creep feeding.

A good example of the principle is seen in the use of PIC farrowing platform. This is almost fully slatted with a small solid area for the sow to lie on and a forward creep for the litter. Layout allows for access all round the platform, which makes for extremely easy handling of the pigs and appears to help with disease control as there is no need for anyone to step inside the pen at any time.

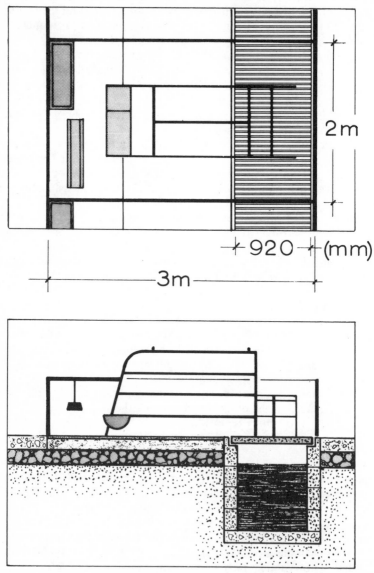

FIG. 24. *Details of farrowing crate with forward creep and partially-slatted floor.*

FORWARD CREEP

For five-week weaning I prefer a covered forward creep which houses the heater and creep feeder. A light may need to be suspended behind or alongside the sow at farrowing and for 24 hours afterwards. Pen divisions can be made of plywood or hardboard, and about 760mm in height. If the sow and litter are to remain in the pen until weaning at five weeks, then water should be provided for the litter with a nipple drinker mounted over the slats.

The design of farrowing crate layout has improved in recent years and attention to detail such as floor finish will give good results if coupled with the correct environmental conditions. Pen width will vary according to the length of time the sow and litter stay in the crate.

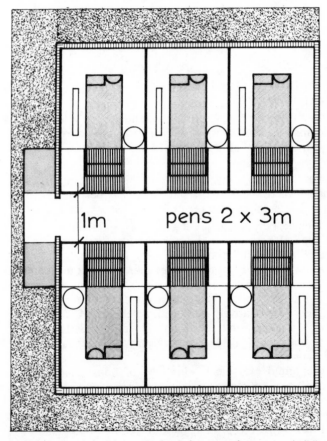

1m

pens 2 x 3m

FIG. 25. *An economical layout for farrowing crates in a narrow building.*

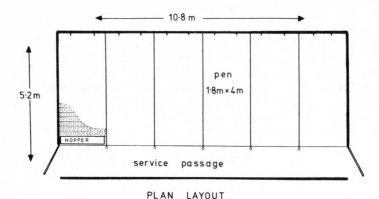

FIG. 26. *Fully slatted container module.*

Three Choices

The main choices appear to be:

(a) Maternity

This is a short-stay, quick-throughput method in which the sows and litters remain for only 10 to 14 days. This will be followed by single or group rearing houses until weaning at five to six weeks.

(b) Maternity/Rearing

The sow and litter stay in the house until weaning at three weeks and this is where the partially slatted floor is particularly useful. The system is also used for weaning at four to five weeks.

(c) Combined Farrowing/Rearing

This type of housing for the sow and litter is falling out of favour because of high capital and labour costs. It is usually linked to eight-week weaning and the layout includes a farrowing crate and creep area. The crate is fixed, on the swinging gate or 'up and over' principle, with the sow initially confined for two or three days before release. Space requirements are relatively high, with a pen size of at least 3m × 3·6m plus passage access, and each 'room' layout holds four or six pens. Cleaning out creates problems and this layout is difficult to fit out with slatted floors.

Another good example of this type of house is the Solari. This simple, effective house uses a voluntary farrowing 'frame' fixed into a long, narrow pen of 5·4m × 1·5m with a creep area at the rear. It is a monopitch house and gives warm draught-free conditions with well-defined farrowing, creep, dunging and feeding areas. Labour requirements are fairly high, access to the creep for feeding is difficult unless this is mechanised, and the voluntary farrowing frame is not so effective in reducing farrowing losses as the fixed farrowing crate.

The combined farrowing/rearing pen has been superseded by the specialised maternity-type house or a two-stage system which uses a crate system for the first few weeks, to be followed by group or single rearing. Many existing Solari-type units have been effectively used as the latter part of this two-stage rearing system for single litters. The weaned pigs can then stay on in the rearing house until they are 31–36kg and ready for the final stages of fattening.

GROUP SUCKLING

This type of housing, in which several sows and litters are grouped together, has always been a traditional part of pig-keeping. It has become more fashionable again recently, with several sows grouped together in specialist yards where the weaners remain until they are

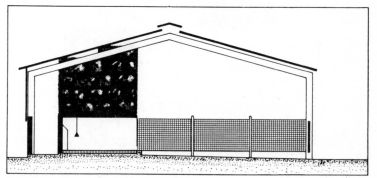

FIG. 27. *General-purpose yards adapted for group suckling of six sows and litters.*

31–36kg liveweight. General-purpose buildings can be adapted and a generous amount of straw is needed.

A long narrow building gives the best shape, with a size of 12·2m × 6·1m for five or six sows and litters. The precise numbers will depend to some extent on the size of the group housed during pregnancy, as one of the main advantages at weaning is that the batch of sows can be moved directly back to dry-sow accommodation without mixing or bullying problems. The number will also require balancing with batch size in the farrowing house. In practice, groups will come down to three to six, otherwise management problems are created. A herd of 100 sows will be required to maintain this sort of batch size and throughput.

Certainly labour demand is reduced, but there is often a second peak of mortality when the sows are moved into the yards from the farrowing crates at 10 to 14 days. At this stage heating will be required in the creep area, along with creep feed and water for the litters. Sow-feeding will often be on the floor with a large cob or nut, but ideally a bank of individual feeders could be shared between several yards and then sows can be fed individually for at least a couple of weeks.

Group suckling is best suited for five- or six-week weaning and I used to find that weaners which had been grouped together were slightly lighter in weight than single suckled litters at weaning, but by ten weeks of age they had made up the difference. Cross suckling can be a problem with this system as the bigger pigs get bigger and the

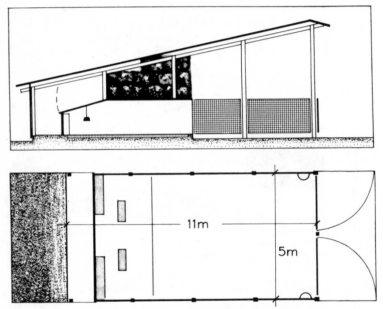

FIG. 28. *Group suckling yards as used at NAC, based on the weaner pool design.*

smaller ones deteriorate, giving a very wide range of pig size. I consider this to be one of the biggest drawbacks to the system.

After the sows have been weaned, yards can be cleaned out with tractor and fore-loader, but in some cases daily cleaning out is preferred. Weaned litters will be *ad lib* fed, which can be automated and equal batches of pigs are drawn out for the fattening houses at the required weight, which will depend on market outlets. Group suckling fits ideally into general-purpose buildings and a straw-based system for five- to six-week weaning, but requires a high standard of management, and a herd with a healthy background.

HOUSING THE WEANER

(a) Tiered Cages—under 21 days of age

During the past few years there has been a revival in early weaning techniques, mostly in the interest of sow productivity. Very specialist housing is needed for the young pig from four to six days up to 10–12 days of age, and for this category the tiered cage has been used. Environmental requirements have already been referred to, but a well-insulated house is needed to maintain precise temperature, ventilation and relative humidity levels. Wire cages with three decks are the usual choice as this saves expensive floor space. Dropping trays are fitted beneath each tier of cages and the house operates on an 'all in, all out' batch system.

Careful control of relative humidity keeps the wire floors fairly dry, and piglets are grouped in batches of six to ten per cage. Nipple drinkers are fitted with a header tank placed inside the house to take the chill off the water. A dry feeding system is used with a pelleted feed and feeding takes place three or four times daily, when the lights are switched on. At other times the houses are in darkness.

Pioneer work in the design and operation of this type of weaner housing took place in Belgium and Holland, and it is clear that a final formula has not yet been arrived at. Cage construction is a specialist job for manufacturers and several firms active in the manufacture of poultry equipment are offering tiered cages for pigs.

A number of companies offer tiered cages housed in container units and these have been both popular and efficient and are used on an increasing number of intensive farms. Heating and ventilation controls have been much improved, and there is no doubt that pigs can be weaned quite successfully on a commercial basis from five to ten days of age. The problem remains one of getting the weaned sow back into pig quickly and regularly and this is still a major stumbling block on all except a few farms.

(b) Flat Deck Cages or Nursery Design

Interest in early weaning has centred around sow productivity and careful management has shown that the early-weaned sow can be got quickly back into pig again.

As a result of this the flat deck or nursery system has emerged as a mainstream system of housing pigs weaned between 17–21 days of age.

A brief guide to current design follows which is based on experience in the United Kingdom and more recent experience in the USA, where a two-stage nursery system has been developed, and which is giving extremely good results on large-scale intensive units.

One of the major areas of interest in design and management of the full confinement unit currently centres around the nursery. This is because there is a growing trend towards earlier weaning at around three weeks of age and a real awareness of the need to look at the pig business on a pigs weaned sow per year basis. The producer must measure the success of his facilities on the number of pigs he can finish out in a year and the cost of doing this.

A brief analysis of the potential of the breeding sow will quickly show that she is capable of weaning 18 to 20 pigs per year but this can only be achieved with three-week weaning on a regular basis year in year out.

Housing for the newly-weaned pig at three weeks of age is critical if these piglets are to survive. European experience in this area goes back about 10 years, when the first specialist nursery buildings appeared. Many lessons have been learned over this period and I would like briefly to set out some of the fundamental principles.

A good piglet is required at about 18 to 20 days of age which is sound, healthy, has been treated for anaemia and is preferably castrated. Ideal weight would be about 5 to 6kg and anything lighter than this should be weaned a week later. It would be helpful if this pig were able to use a nipple drinker and was at least familiar with solid food from daily creep feeding whilst still on the sow.

'All-In, All-Out'

A firm rule for success in operating any early-weaning system is to work on an 'all-in, all-out' basis. Ideally, a nursery room should have sufficient capacity for one week's weaning. For instance, a 480-sow unit would have a mating target of 24 per week with a weekly farrowing of 20 litters per week. Room size would then be in the region of 180–200 weaners. This is sometimes difficult to achieve with older units, but when converting and at change of herd size, the opportunity should be taken to set things in balance. This means complete compartmentalisation with separate ventilation, control equipment, heating and manure disposal. Mixed age groups of weaners in nursery systems can make it almost impossible to manage and control minor scours, and disease problems then become major disasters.

Thermal Environment

Temperature levels and control are of vital importance to the newly-weaned pig, whose heat regularity control is poorly developed and who has at this stage very little fat cover over vital organs. Temperatures to aim for are 27 to 29°C during the first seven to ten days after weaning, dropping by 1 or 2°C weekly down to about 21°C when the pigs are six to seven weeks of age. Holding the temperature steady and avoiding fluctuations on a day and night basis is as important as holding the overall temperatures. Wide changes in temperatures will trigger off chills and predispose to scours and other intestinal problems. Supplementary heat will be required to achieve these temperatures and this needs linking in with insulation and ventilation rates.

Manure Disposal

Worldwide experience clearly shows that nursery design should be based on a fully slatted floor. Rapid separation of the young pig from its faeces and urine seems to be extremely important—even if this factor is difficult to quantify in scientific terms. In a similar way the dung needs removal from underneath the slats as quickly as possible. A woven wire floor with a flushing system or 'pull the plug' design seems to come nearest to meeting these design system considerations.

Single or Multi-Deck

My experience along with many other producers and managers would lead me to recommend a single-deck system in preference to two- or three-tier systems. The main advantage of the single deck is in the all-around ease of observation, pig handling, feeding and management. Moreover, ventilation and heating in single deck is very difficult without the added complication of several tiers. A case can be argued for multi-tiers on the grounds of capital cost but I believe this can be a mistake in the day-to-day operation of the nursery. I do prefer a design with the single deck in which the pigs are lifted above the floor height about 0·6m to 0·75m. This keeps them clear of any floor draughts and allows for good observation and handling as well as allowing construction of manure pits to be above ground level for lower building costs.

Two-Stage Nursery

One of the main problems with early nursery designs involved trying to design facilities that would provide acceptable environments for the newly-weaned pig at 5 to 6kg and the feeder pig ready to leave the system at 22–24kg liveweight. In the end, these compromise designs proved difficult to operate and results were very disappointing. This problem area was largely resolved by further specialisation and subdivision of nurseries into a two-stage system—a pre-nursery followed by the nursery proper. The pig is weaned into a pre-nursery which has sufficient small pens to allow all litters to be housed on an individual litter basis. Pigs stay in the pre-nursery for two to three weeks and then move into the nursery for a further three to four-week period where they are grouped in pens of 18–20 pigs per pen, which dovetails neatly into grower and finisher accommodations.

The pre-nursery system allows better care and control with litter groups. It also eliminates mixing, stress and fighting immediately at weaning when immunity patterns are at their lowest and when violent changes are being forced on the digestive tract of the newly-weaned pig when it moves from a liquid to a solid diet.

By using this system, mortality rates have been markedly reduced and at the same time growth rates have been improved with increased food intake. The pre-nursery system also allows more careful and specific control of temperatures and ventilation rates. When the pigs are about five weeks of age they can then be transferred out of litter groups as they are sorted into the nursery. This is then a relatively strong pig now, well used to eating a solid diet with disease immunity building up and well able to take the stress of mixing and moving. This move also provides an opportunity to match weights, sizes, males and females more closely and evenly than at three weeks of age. The case for the two-stage nursery is now well established and should be a major priority in planning new facilities or in updating older ones.

With well-designed facilities, skilful management and a good healthy source of pigs, it is absolutely essential to provide the early-weaned pig with the correct diet. Actual cost per ton should not be a major concern as newly-weaned pigs only eat a few pounds of this high-cost feed and the returns in improved liveweight gain and reduction in mortality fully justify the extra costs.

Capacity and Throughput

To allow feeder pigs to be sold at 18–20kg liveweight and using a two-stage nursery system with pigs weaned at three weeks of age, then seven rooms will be required each capable of holding one week's weaning from 20 sows, approximately 180–200 pigs.

This should then be split down into three pre-nursery rooms and four nursery rooms. This should allow sufficient time for washing out, disinfecting and drying between each batch. If the farrowing section is based on 80 crates, then extra breathing space can be gained by adding another pre-nursery to make four of each type. Either of these systems should then be capable of producing 180–200 feeder pigs at 18–20kg for sale or transfer and in total an annual output of between 8,500–9,500 pigs.

Room and Pen Size

Room shape and size will vary with the overall design of the facility but I strongly recommend a room with a central passage with raised decks either side. This is a simple layout giving good access and visibility. In the pre-nursery pen size would be $1.2m \times 1.2m$ with a central passage of 1 metre with 10 pens either side. Overall dimensions would be in the region of $12m \times 3.5m$. This square pen holds one litter group and has a fully slatted floor. This gives about $1.13m^2$ per pig when feeder space is taken out, which is a standard figure for a pre-nursery pig between 5.4 and 9kg.

Nursery design is based on a similar layout with central passage and pens either side. However, fewer pens are required as litters are mixed into groups of 18–20 by size and sex and 10 pens will be sufficient. This layout gives a room size of approximately $7{\cdot}2m \times 7{\cdot}5m$. An alternative frequently used in Europe is based on a longer, narrower room with side passage of $1{\cdot}0m$ and 10 pens in a continuous row giving a room size of $15 \times 4{\cdot}2m$. The important factor is to use a room principle based on weekly farrowings and then to match these rooms into a balanced layout linked to a central service passageway. Again a raised flat deck is used about 60–76cm above the passageway, keeping the pigs away from floor draughts and allowing good observation. Individual pen size of $3 \times 1{\cdot}5m$ of fully slatted floor allows almost $0{\cdot}22m^2$ per weaner which will be more than adequate for the feeder pig at 18–20kg liveweight.

Ventilation, Heating and Insulation

Space will only allow me to deal with some principles on this subject which are fundamental for the early-weaning system to work successfully. Walls should contain at least the equivalent of 10cm of glass wool and internal plywood cladding. The ceiling should contain at least 15cm of glass wool or equivalent. Ventilation remains a key factor and at the same time a temperature of at least 26°C must be maintained in the pre-nursery. Clearly supplemental heating will be needed and most systems now use solid-state electronic controls which sense temperatures and synchronise and automatically control heaters and ventilation fans. Ventilation rates for growing pigs from 9 to 18kg have been well defined and are generally quoted as $0{\cdot}04m^3/hr/kg$ or a maximum $0{\cdot}2m^3/hr/kg$, depending on age and size at removal.

The problem arises with the smaller pig at 5–6kg at weaning, especially in cold weather and low stocking rates, as requirements are probably lower than those quoted above. It becomes difficult to run large fans at low speeds with sufficient accuracy to control air speeds so that special small fans are needed or, better still, some form of motorised inlet control should be used with the larger fans. As a principle, I prefer to bring in fresh air through a ducted ceiling system, preferably with automatic operation. This allows good control and mixing of air within the building which is followed by exhaustion of foul air below pit level by using a fully slatted floor system. In Europe the air would be pressurised or forced into the building at ridge of gable and exhausted below slat through a baffle system. In the USA a fan system is often preferred which is used to pull out foul air from below slats.

Supplementary heat can be provided in the duct system or by heaters suspended within the building. In some areas at some periods of the year cooling may be essential and a roof intake with a ducting system is ideal for this. Heating costs must be carefully watched but depending on the type of fuel used it can be fairly safely stated that providing the building is well insulated then it is cheaper to provide extra heat for the building rather than extra feed for the pigs. In any case supplementary heat is essential when a room is first occupied with newly-weaned pigs, especially with below-zero temperatures typical of the Midwest, and also for drying out between batches. With any heating and ventilation system for young pigs an alarm system should be fitted. This can be linked to a phone system or perhaps operate a 'drop out' door if temperatures get too high—say above 35°C.

This critical phase of piglet rearing is certain to require energy for supplementary heating. Equipment designers and farmers are just beginning to look at some alternatives to electricity and LP gas. Natural gas is good value if there is a local supply, but other systems now coming into use include solar energy and below-ground or geo-thermal sources. I am certain we are going to see some interesting and exciting developments in the area of alternative energy sources.

Materials and Construction

I am particularly concerned with internal construction and specifically with floors. Over 10 years of experience in the area has taught me that the best material for flooring for the young pig is metal wire. Currently galvanised woven wire is the best product as it gives reasonable pig comfort whilst minimising foot damage and is relatively self-cleaning.

A galvanised wire should give a life of 7 to 10 years. I have tried many other products over the past 15 years, using timber, plastics, concrete and other materials, but can state with confidence that woven wire is the best product available. Internal pen divisions can also be made from a wide range of materials. Hog panels, wire mesh, or vertical tubular bars are probably the best choice. This allows litters and pigs to see each other and allows better movement of air within the building, always providing floor draughts have been eliminated by the raised deck.

Manure Removal

The basic concept must be to remove manure from below decks as frequently as possible. This can be achieved in a number of ways but the simplest is by a 'pull the plug' method into an underground sewer system. Where water is not a major consideration then a flush system probably provides the most complete answer since this can be operated automatically several times during the day. The extra cost is probably worthwhile and the long, narrow building will reduce the number of flush tanks required. Solid/liquid separation and recirculation systems provide a very good answer to manure removal from inside the confinement building where water may be in short supply. At the same time this will improve the internal environment for both pigs and staff by removing gases and odours.

Feeding and Watering Systems

Pre-nursery and nursery should be treated separately. In the pre-nursery it is essential to have a long, narrow trough for the litter group to feed all at once. Remember that the mob instinct of feeding simultaneously during suckling is still very strong with the early-weaned pig. I advise that these pigs should be fed little and often, up to six to eight times through the working day. A trough about $1 \cdot 0$ to $1 \cdot 1$m will do the job, allowing about 10cm trough space per pig. This type of approach to feeding will also create competition at feeding time in the pre-nursery which encourages feed intake at a critical time. Feed should be conveyed automatically to a feed truck in the house which can then be used for distribution by hand scoop to each litter group.

In the nursery a fence line feeding can be used which is shared between two pens and can almost stretch the full length of the 3m pen division. Because pigs in the nursery are well past any post-weaning check period their feed can be supplied with automatic feed systems, although these are better to be filled on a daily basis to allow time for observation of the pigs at this stage.

All nursery pens should be fitted with at least two nipple drinkers per pen sited at the opposite end of the pen to the feeder to encourage traffic across the floor. The drinkers should be linked to a header tank and should be capable of being switched to a water medication system in a few minutes. Whatever the system of management, there will be occasions when some form of medication is required.

Capital Costs

Specific costs are difficult to determine because they are usually part of an overall facility/complex figure. However, the best way to arrive at a cost is to work on a pound cost per square metre. This will vary with the type of system provided. Obviously complicated heating and ventilation systems will push up the cost, but the range will vary from £150 per square metre for basic facilities up to £200 per square metre for a complete system with flushing facilities. These should be treated as guidelines only and for contract work. Local labour and farm staff will be able to operate at lower rates to reduce these figures.

Pig Performance

The overall target must be to cut down on the traditional post-weaning check. This is usually more severe with the early-weaned pig, and raised nursery decks in both Europe and America have shown that this check can be avoided. A good performance target to aim for is to get to 22kg at 10 weeks of age as feeder pigs come out of the nursery. This could be achieved at a daily gain of 330g per pig and a range between 318 to 410g should be the target to go for.

Feed per kg of gain should be in the range of 1·5 to 2·0, depending to a large extent on the energy and nutritional make-up of the feed. Feed usage per pig will range between 0·5 and 0·6kg per pig per day and good trough design and feeding methods should make sure that most of this is eaten by the pig and not wasted below slat. Perhaps the biggest gain will be in the reduction in mortality and a target of below 1 per cent should be the figure to go for.

To summarise, I believe raised nursery decks have a very important role to play in successful pig confinement systems.

It is essential to start with the right pig, to use a well-balanced milk-based diet and to follow the health rules with an 'all-in, all-out' system. A raised deck with a fully slatted floor will make observation and management easier and manure must be removed frequently from below the slats. Temperature control is vital, and providing these basic rules are followed then the post-weaning check of the early weaned pig should be a thing of the past.

THREE-WEEK WEANING

(a) Out of Doors

Outdoor systems based on the use of the straw bale shelter and fenced paddocks on light dry land were developed by BOCM/Silcock at Stoke Mandeville. Labour requirements were fairly high and in wetter areas on heavy land a portable weaning ark gave better results. A wooden hut provided a kennel area about 2·4m × 1·8m with access through a pophole to an outdoor run with a weldmesh floor. A sliding lid covered the kennel area which was adjustable for ventilation. This design gave a good sound construction with a low, warm sleeping area and a slatted dunging run. In winter these portable huts were drawn up onto a concrete pad. Eventually the units were planned on a permanent basis so that water would be laid on, with hard road access for feeding and servicing. Two or three litters were placed in each pen at 5·4kg liveweight and stayed on until they were 22–27kg liveweight.

These outdoor units produced good healthy pigs but were not entirely the best working conditions for stockmen, and this led directly to the development of the intensive verandah weaner house which is now an integral part of many of our large-scale commercial pig farms.

(b) Verandah Weaner House

The prefabricated weaner house is based on a central covered passage which gives access for feeding and servicing. On either side of this

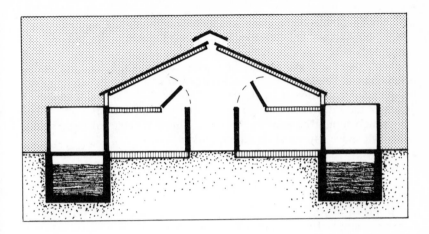

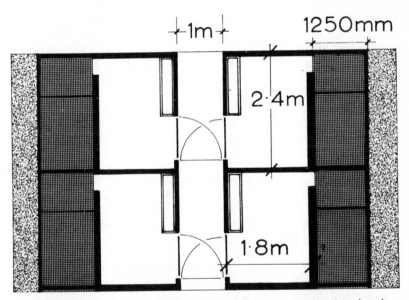

FIG. 29. *Verandah weaner house with central kennels and outer slatted yards.*

passage there are 2·4m × 1·3m pens which are covered by hinged lids. The construction is of timber studding covered by 9·5mm asbestos with an insulation infill. There is a pophole to an outside dunging area which has a weldmesh floor and in which the drinker is placed. The sleeping/feeding kennel floor is insulated with a no-fines concrete. Feeding is by hopper, and ideally the house is best suited to the five- to six-week weaner. Three litters are placed in at about 11kg liveweight, then at 18kg they are sub-divided into two batches of 15 and stay on until they reach 27–31kg liveweight.

With careful management the house can be used for three-week weaners but floor space will need reduction and extra heating may be required. Ventilation is by natural means, with the kennel lid used to control the rate. The outside runs are placed over a continuous slurry pit which should be about 1·2m deep. Slurry is removed periodically through sluice gates or by vacuum tanker.

By careful control of stocking densities the internal pen remains clean and dry and the combination of warm kennel and fresh air gives very good results. The pigs will be *ad lib* fed at first, but as they approach 22–27kg liveweight they can be switched to floor feeding before removal to the fattening houses. Water is provided in the slatted area through nipple drinkers or self-fill water bowls. Portable drinkers may be needed for three-week weaning and with this size of pig in winter or in exposed situations it may be necessary to cover the outdoor pen with a canopy of slotted oil-tempered hardboard or framed corrugated plastic sheet.

This type of weaner house is built in blocks of 12 to 16 pens, as natural ventilation does not work very well on very long runs. Weaners are put into the house through the central passage which has a service door into each pen. Labour requirements are low, observation of pigs is very good. This house, when used for five- to six-week weaning provides a very good practical solution for weaner accommodation. For earlier weaning the flat deck cage is a better commercial answer.

WEANERS
The Weaner Pool

This is an old pig husbandry system which has been brought up to date and linked successfully with the use of controlled-environment houses. A wide range of buildings can be used—cattle yards, general-purpose buildings or the specialist weaner pool. A generous amount of straw is used for bedding and a group size of 40 to 50 is ideal with an 'all in, all out' system. Weaners can be put in the pool at 11·2–13·6kg liveweight and in fact the second stage of the group suckling system doubles up as the weaner pool.

The building should be oblong in shape, preferably twice as long as wide, i.e., 9·7m × 4·8m. At least one-third of the area at the back of the yard should be kennelled and this will provide straw storage for the essential daily bedding down. Two water bowls should be provided, and they may need protection from frost. Cleaning is carried out by tractor and foreloader—after pigs are moved out into fattening accommodation.

Pen divisions are best built of concrete blocks but 13mm asbestos, well supported, is just as good, but should be placed on a dwarf concrete wall to prevent tractor and foreloader damage. The floor of the kennel area needs insulation and in winter the front of the kennel can be blocked in with the *ad lib* feeders. The front gates will need cladding, as this naturally ventilated housing system must provide draught-free conditions at pig level.

The Bought-in Weaner

Variations on the weaner yard have been used for the bought-in weaner as there is usually some mixing or re-grouping to be done. Deep straw with lots of space probably provide the best reception it is possible to supply for the bought-in weaner. Overall space allowance amounts to 0·92m² per pig, of which one-third will be in the covered kennel.

THE FATTENING PIG

A wide choice of housing for the fattening pig still exists. The market outlet—pork, bacon or manufacturing—will determine to some extent the exact form of housing, but strong local variations can be found. The sweat box, as developed in Northern Ireland, is a good example of this, or the 'squattie' in Cornwall. I intend to concentrate on three examples which illustrate good pig fattening house design and which meet most present-day requirements.

Trobridge

This is a simple house of original design based on the old 'cottager's sty', but using modern materials. The building has a monopitch roof (height at rear 1·06m, at front 2·2m) with an overall floor size of 4·5m × 2·4m. The lying area is separated from the dunging area by an adjustable 'strawboard'. It is naturally ventilated, with an adjustable flap in the rear wall and a 0·6m deep adjustable shutter above the pen fronts.

House construction is mainly of 13mm exterior-grade plywood for roof, rear and side walls, but insulated blocks could be used for the walls. The front gates are made of timber hurdles lined with asbestos partition board. Floor feeding is carried out through a flap in the roof, 1·2m × 1·2m, which can also be used for increasing ventilation.

The original design was based on a solid floor with straw bedding, but a slatted variation has been used successfully. This house provides accommodation for 18 to 20 pork pigs (slaughter weight 63kg) or 12 to 14 bacon pigs (90kg liveweight). The pigs are placed in at weaning and then split down to final numbers. The solid-floor house makes a good reception base for bought-in weaners or for on-farm performance

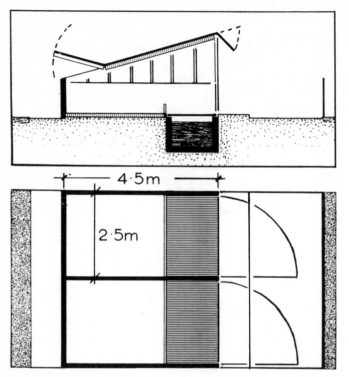

FIG. 30. *Trobridge fattening pens with partially-slatted floors.*

testing of litter groups. A passage for access at the rear is essential and a tractor scraping apron across the front will reduce the fairly high labour requirement, as daily cleaning out is based on brush and squeegee. Hoppers can be placed in the pen for *ad lib* feeding, but have to be serviced through the front gate, and automatic drinkers are fixed in the dunging area.

The natural ventilation in this building calls for considerable skill and judgement by the stockman if temperature is to be kept steady. The unit allows flexible management and the floor to roof partitions give good isolation between pens.

Stockmen are operating out of doors and the house needs linking with a race and yard for weighing pigs. Feed mechanisation is difficult, but this fattening house is invaluable on any pig farm because of its utility for all classes of pigs. The solid-floor type is more suited to the medium-sized herd because of labour demand, but the partially-slatted floor Trobridge has been used widely on a number of large commercial units.

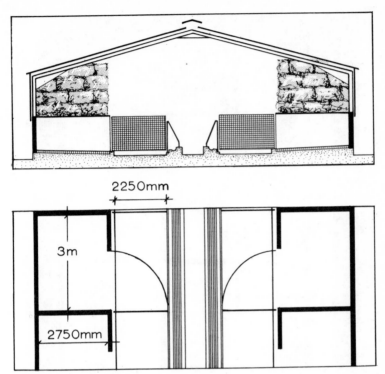

FIG. 31. *Suffolk-type feeding house with outer kennels under fully-covered yard.*

Suffolk Type

As the name indicates, this type of housing was developed in East Anglia with straw-based systems and general-purpose framed buildings. These features were linked to tractor scraping of solid manure, some straw storage, and troughs with pipeline feeding. Two particular models have been developed in recent years, one with the kennels against the outer wall, the other with a central kennel layout and given the name of 'zig-zag'. Pigs come into the building at 27–31kg liveweight in groups of 12 to 15 to match the pen size and stay through to bacon or cutter weight. Labour demand is fairly low, with mechanical feeding and thrice weekly cleaning out by tractor and scraper.

The pigs lie back in a warm kennel and observation of the pigs is particularly good in the zig-zag type of house. Straw is stored above the pens, which provides material to hand for daily bedding down, and with the zig-zag advantage can be taken of ridge height for extra storage capacity. Two feed passages are required, but these can also be used for weighing and handling of pigs. A clear span-framed building

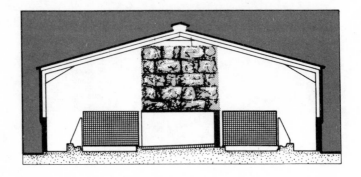

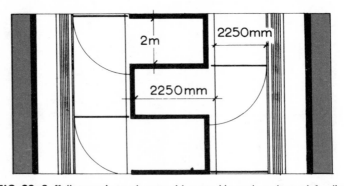

FIG. 32. *Suffolk-type zig-zag layout with central kennels and trough feeding.*

of timber, steel or concrete is the best choice for this type of building, but farm-built concrete block walls with timber trusses work equally well.

The overall building width required is at least 10·9m with feed passages of 1·06m and scraped passages 2·2m. Careful design is needed for trough and pen fronts. A half-round salt-glazed 305mm trough with either tubular rails or high tensile wires completes the pen fronts. Gates should be made of square section steel framework and clad with weldmesh, and have a pig-proof slide-type fastener. In the zig-zag, gate posts can be fastened together with a metal strap across the top of the kennel. Pen floor insulation is desirable and with straw bedding a strawboard at the open front will save on bedding costs.

Drinkers can be mounted above the kerb in the scraping passage out of the way of the tractor. At least 305mm of trough run per pig place will be required, so that this factor determines pen shape and overall house design and layout. Internal walls are built of 102mm or 152mm concrete blocks which should be 'bag washed' and then treated with a waterproof paint.

The roof material for the kennel can be plywood or tongue and groove mounted on strong runners because of the weight of straw to be carried. Space boarding down the side of the building provides natural ventilation with outlet through a raised ridge. Roof cladding will be of corrugated asbestos or steel sheets.

This type of house is easy to operate and is not very demanding from a management point of view. Both zig-zag and outer kennels have their strong points, but pen shape is probably better and warmer in the central zig-zag. This layout is also free of frame stanchions which may be in the way with outer kennels. There is no doubt that the modern Suffolk type is an effective design for a farm with home-grown cereals and on-farm food preparation with pipeline feeding.

HOUSING FATTENERS

Enclosed, partially slatted house

This type of house has been developed over the last ten years and featured in the first type of 'package deal' in the pig-housing market. Whilst the construction and design were adequate, the management techniques at farm level had not been worked out. Fortunately this problem has now been largely resolved, and these points are discussed in the chapter on management—Chapter 8. House design and layout have been improved, with a long, narrow pen as the best choice.

Pig farmers have worked out a management plan which moves the pigs into the house at about 31–33·2kg liveweight, which reduces the weight spread within the house and makes for better stocking rates and cleaner pens. Environmental conditions have been fairly well defined and control equipment for regulation of temperature and ventilation is now extremely reliable and well developed. All this leads to standardisation and prefabrication, and much progress has been made with this approach. Pigs coming into the house at 31–33·2kg from verandah weaner houses or flat decks will already be familiar with partially slatted floors, floor feeding and nipple drinkers. After a brief settling-in period pigs grow extremely quickly, putting on 4–5·4kg per week until their removal for slaughter as cutters or bacon pigs.

A labour-saving mechanised dry-feeding system should be fitted and this will be operated automatically three or four times a day, dispensing a precise amount of nuts or pellets on the floor. The house lights go on at feeding time, otherwise a low-intensity lighting pattern is adopted which is sufficient for observation and inspection.

The prefabricated construction will almost certainly include timber walls and gables with a corrugated asbestos or steel roof. Internal cladding will be of flat asbestos sheeting or oil-tempered hardboard and internal divisions of square-section steel bolted onto upright stanchions.

The bottom portion of the divisions is fitted with a fillet of 13mm asbestos sheet to prevent food being pushed from pen to pen.

Overall pen size is 4·5m × 1·8m with an area of 1·2m × 1·8m slatted against the outside wall of the house. The pen floor is insulated and the slatted area is made up of concrete panels. The slat gap should be 13mm with a 50–76mm solid portion running at right angles to the building. There should be a gradual fall towards the slats, with direct access for the pigs to their dunging area and to the nipple drinker mounted over the slats. Slurry stored under the slats is released through sluice gates or removed by vacuum tanker as required.

There has been much discussion over ventilation but the best method is to mount the extractor fans on the side wall and draw air in through the ridge. The baffled ridge inlets are then controlled from the central feed and service passage. Ventilation is controlled by thermostats carefully sited within the building.

A central service area between sections of the house can be used for weighing pigs and for housing feed and environmental controls. This service area can be used to split up very large buildings into rooms holding 300 to 400 pigs of similar size and weight. This type of house is now typical of our larger intensive units, even in the arable areas. Prefabrication has brought the capital cost well below the equivalent semi-intensive general-purpose building.

Labour requirements are extremely low, but good slurry handling facilities are essential. Mechanical feeding has removed almost all the physical drudgery out of this stage of pig production and a very high standard of management is required—and being achieved. This form of broiler pig production appears to be the basis for future pig-production systems.

Enclosed, fully slatted house

Now that the flat deck system has become firmly established, it seems entirely logical to use a similar fully slatted house for finishing the pigs through to slaughter weight. House design is based on a fully insulated shell similar to the partially slatted house. Pens are laid out either side of a central access/service passage which should be 1·2m wide with pen size approximately 4·5m × 2·0m. Pen floors can be made up of weldmesh, expanded metal, perforated panels (both galvanised) or well-designed concrete slats.

Ventilation would be similar to systems used in flat decks but without the supplementary heating. Air is drawn into the building through a false perforated or fibre-glass ceiling or through ducting and exhausted below slat level.

Pens, as indicated earlier, will hold 12 to 15 pigs through to 90kg with a choice of two feeding systems. Floor feeding is of course ruled

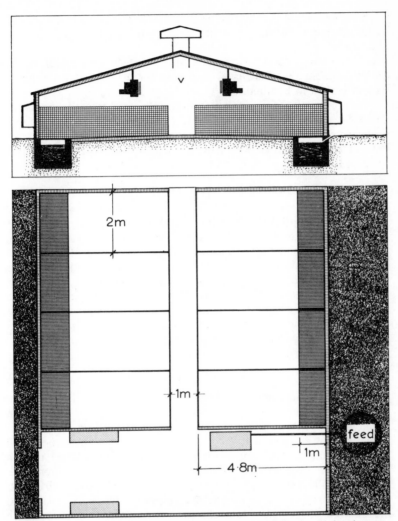

FIG. 33. *Feeding house with controlled ventilation, partially-slatted dunging areas and long narrow pens for floor feeding.*

out so that *ad lib* feeding could be used with a feed hopper forming the front of the pen adjacent to the service passage. Some genetically improved herds, especially where gilts and boars are separated, will use this sytem, but an alternative is to provide a half-round trough down the long side of the pen, which gives adequate feeding space for all 15 pigs.

This system should of course be linked to a semi- or fully-automatic feeding system as feeding by hand in such a trough would be virtually impossible.

Slurry removal from below slat can be achieved by a sluicing or flushing system but there is a good case for a below-slat automatic scraper system to be fitted.

I believe that UK farmers will increasingly move towards the use of the fully slatted floor system because of economy of labour and simplicity in operation. The real problem remains one of capital cost, but this can be justified with a well-designed house that will operate for 7 to 10 years.

LOADING AND TRANSPORT

Loading Ramps

Finally, loading facilities for the pig leaving the farm for slaughter. A well-designed layout should provide room for a loading ramp which, for health reasons, is best sited outside the main unit. Ideally a covered area is needed, but a ramp with good access for large haulage vehicles will save endless time and trouble with pigs being loaded for slaughter.

This is an area of pig housing which has been neglected, but a renewed interest is being taken in the movement, handling, and transport of the live meat pig to the point of slaughter.

Care in loading and transporting of pigs will give better meat quality and fewer losses from carcase condemnations.

PEN REQUIREMENTS

With new units there is a need—and an opportunity—to plan housing requirements precisely. This will save capital costs and smooth the flow of pigs through the various stages of production. Bottlenecks in the system are avoided, leaving labour time for management and recording, and allowing contract requirements—which will be based on a time period—to be fulfilled. With existing units expansion often takes place gradually, but there is still a necessity to check pen requirements occasionally, otherwise too many pigs appear in the wrong place and may cause management and health problems. Changes in policy, such as a move to group suckling or three-week weaning may throw pen requirements out of gear.

Allowances will have to be made for cleaning out, disinfection, and resting programmes, and pen requirements will obviously be dependent on pig performance. In the following examples and calculations a farrowing index of 2·0 is used with nine pigs reared per litter, or 18 per sow per year. The growth rate of the feeding pigs is taken as 4·5kg weight gain per week after 27kg liveweight. However, at the end of the day extra pens will always be needed for the odd sick or injured pig, for isolation, for breeding gilts if these have been bought in, and for catering for those emergencies which arise on the best planned farms!

Pen Requirements—How to Work These Out

Farrow Places—100-sow Unit

Farrowing Index 2·0, with five-week weaning, litters staying in the crates all the time. An allowance is made for one week before farrowing and one week after the pigs are removed.

Farrowings per year $100 \times 2 \cdot 0 = 200$, with a seven-week occupation period, as previously described:

Farrowings per pen $\dfrac{52}{7} = 7$ approx.

No. of pens required $= \dfrac{200}{7} = 30$ approx.

To allow for batching, 32 pens would be about the right number.

Dry-sows Places—100 Sows; Five-week Weaning

Suckling for five weeks, but one week in a crate before farrowing. Therefore, at two litters per year, a period of $(2 \times 6) = 12$ weeks away from dry-sow housing leaving balance of 40 weeks.

$$\frac{40 \times 100}{52} = 77 \text{ places.}$$

In practice, with culling rate at about 15 per cent after weaning, the sow stall requirements would be about 66–70 places.

Fattening Places—Bacon Pigs

With pigs entering at 31kg and leaving at 90kg then four batches per year can be achieved. For our 100-sow unit we require

$$\frac{100 \times 18}{4} = 450.$$

In practice, 500 pig places would be needed to allow for uneven batches and fluctuations in throughput, which at 15 per pen means about 34 pens.

Pen Requirements

EXAMPLE A: 100-sow unit.
Straw-based group housing and sow yards.
Crate farrowing followed by:
Group suckling.
Five- to six-week weaning.
Bacon (75 per cent), pork (25 per cent).

Dry Sows and Boars
18 yards each holding four sows.
Four boar pens.

Farrowing
20 crates—four rooms, each with four crates
        —four single crates.

Group Suckling
12 pens each holding four sows (from two to three weeks until 11 to 12 weeks).

Fattening
36 pens each holding 15 pigs.
eg, two houses each with 18 pens.

EXAMPLE B: 250-sow unit.
Slatted floor—individual sow housing.
Sow stalls.
Crate farrowing.
Four- to five-week weaning.
Verandah weaner housing.
Bacon production 90kg.

Dry Sows and Boars
180 sow stalls—including six boar pens.
Four yards for gilt reception and two boar pens.

Farrowing
76 farrowing pens.
Nine rooms with eight crates and one room with four crates.

Weaners
30 pens. Each pen taking three litters:
        i.e., 30 pigs at weaning, then later splitting down to 15 per pen.

Fattening
72 pens each taking 15 pigs. I would suggest two houses, each with 36 pens.

EXAMPLE C: 200 sows, 3-week weaning.
Sow stall housing.
Crate farrowing.
Flat deck rearing.
Bacon to 90kg.

Dry Sows and Boars
160 stalls with six boar pens.
Three yards for gilt reception with two boar pens.

Farrowing
40 crates in four rooms, each of 10 crates.

Flat Deck (5kg to 30kg)
36 pens each holding 12–15 pigs,
preferably six rooms each with six pens.

Fattening (30kg to 90kg)
72 pens each holding 15 pigs;
approx. 1,100 places.

EXAMPLE D: 100 sows.
Straw and group housing.
Service area.
Stalls or tethers.
Maternity farrowing.
Single rearing.
Five- to six-week weaning.
Pork production (63kg liveweight).

Dry Sows and Boars
Service area: 12 to 18 places including gilts.
            four boar places.
Stalls or tethers: 50 to 60 places.

Farrowing
12 farrowing crates.

Rearing
28 rearing pens (single) until 15·8kg liveweight.

Fattening
22 Trobridge pens, each holding 18 to 20 pigs.

EXAMPLE E: 70 sows, selling weaners.
Individual sow housing.
Stalls or tethers.
Crate farrowing.
Three-week weaning.
Flat deck cages.
Pigs sold at 20kg.

Dry Sows and Boars
55 stalls or tethers.
Three boar pens.
One gilt yard.

Farrowing
20 farrowing places.
Four rooms of four.
Four single crates.

Flat Deck
20 pens holding 12–15 pigs/pen,
preferably in five rooms with four pens in each room.

COSTS

Initial capital cost will often be the first consideration when a pig project is in the planning stages, so I am making an attempt to put a figure on the various types of pig housing at the present time (1980).

The costings are measured in terms of cost per sow place and cost per pig place. This is a crude and approximate method but it gives some indication on a relative basis and, while actual prices will vary from year to year, they should remain proportionally more or less the same. More sophisticated methods, such as cost per square metre, could be used, but these must then take into account stocking density, through-put, and husbandry systems.

The following assumptions are made:

(1) Current costs based on prices in January 1980.
(2) All prices are before grant, where applicable.
(3) A level, accessible site is assumed, with all work carried out by specialist contractors.

Dry sows	£ *per Sow*
Outdoors on extensive system	25–35
Yards fully covered—with feeders	130–150
Yards semi-covered	80–100
Yards semi-covered—shared feeders	55–65
Sow cubicles in general-purpose stall	100–110
Stall, part slatted, including boar pens	140–160
Stalls, solid floors, including boar pens	100–110
Tethers—part-slatted floors	110–130
Tethers—solid floor	90–100
Boar yards with shared service area	330–480

Sows and Litters	£ *per sow and litter*
Maternity crate—part-slatted	480–700
Maternity crate—fully-slatted	670–770
Solari type	220–260
Single litter follow on	230–310
Group suckling—general purpose	230–280
Group suckling	200–240

Rearing	£ *per pig place*
Flat deck	30–50
Weaner pool—conversion	12–25
Weaner pool—specialist conversion	25–35
Weaner verandah, part-slatted	20–25

Fattening	
Suffolk-type, zig-zag	45–55
Trobridge—solid floors	30–35
—part-slatted	40–45
Fully enclosed, part-slatted	45–55
Fully enclosed, fully-slatted	60–80

NOTE: If automatic feeding is planned in fattening then there will be an extra cost per pig place in the range of £10–£20 per pig.

Complete Unit—Breeding and Fattening

Cost per sow place	£750–£1,250

This list of prices is, of necessity, a very general figure. Prices will vary according to locality, availability of local labour, and, when base work accounts for almost half the cost of the total building, the extent to which farm staff are involved in the operation. Obviously, the larger the project the more favourable the price per pig, and access to services such as hard roads, water, and electricity will play a large part in determining the final price of the contract.

Some farmers are willing and capable of undertaking the construction and erection of some of these buildings themselves. With careful planning and sound advice, they may be able to trim some of the prices by 15 per cent to 20 per cent, but there are no short cuts in specialist livestock housing, and for a short-term gain the long-term performance of the animals and the profitability of the unit, may suffer.

Chapter 7

FEEDING

THE IMPORTANCE of feed in pig production cannot be over-emphasised. In straight economic terms food costs account for 75–80 per cent of the total costs of pig production in the feeding herd, and 60–65 per cent in the breeding herd. Moreover, there are important interactions with other aspects of pig production such as the genetic merit of the pig, housing standards, and management practices.

Since the energy crises of 1973 the price of raw feed materials has changed dramatically. At one time the UK market was isolated from world trading conditions but this situation has changed, with Russia in particular buying grain from the USA. Amongst other factors this led to a world shortage of cereal grains, and with the increasing cost of inflation, animal feed products reached record levels. The ratio of feed costs in relation to the price of the end meat product has forced many UK pig farmers out of business, and it is only since the record harvest in August/September of 1977 that pig feed prices have eased back.

All this emphasises the importance of feedingstuffs, with a focus on its nutrient quality, the search for alternative ingredients, and the need for greater precision in feed levels and feeding methods.

This book does not set out to detail the nutrient requirements of various classes of pigs, as this has been the basis for a large amount of current experimental and research work which is well documented. Neither do I intend to set out a long list of pig food ingredients and their composition, as these have been published by a number of authorities in articles and text-books on pig nutrition.

The most recently published book on this topic is called *Practical Pig Nutrition* by C. T. Whittemore and F. W. H. Elsley (Farming Press). This first-class book describes in some detail the objectives, background details and practical application of pig nutrition and should be a first reference for advisers and farmers involved in pig production.

Another standard reference on pig nutritional requirements is the ARC booklet, *The Nutrient Requirements of Farm Livestock. No. 3, Pigs*. These standards, published in 1967, were based on evidence collected up to 1964, and are clearly in need of bringing up to date. *Nutrient Requirements of Swine*, 6th Revised edition, 1968, published in the USA, is also widely used as a reference in this country. Pig nutrition must be checked continually against changes in breeding stock, housing standards and levels of management.

Pigs vary considerably in their ability to make the best use of different diets and raw materials, and ingredients vary widely in their nutrient make-up. The ARC realised the problems by stating 'Outside of our terms of reference are such matters as the most profitable level of yield. These and other similar questions are highly relevant to the feed compounder and the farmer, and their resolution requires close co-operation at all stages between biologists, economists, and statisticians.'

The pig can only perform economically and profitably if it consumes, on a daily basis, the appropriate amount of energy, protein, vitamins and minerals. A brief description of the energy and protein requirements of the pig, as they are known at present, may lead to a better understanding of practical pig feeding.

ENERGY

The energy content of a food is used by the pig in a number of ways including the following:

(1) Maintenance of heartbeat, blood circulation, cell replacement and other bodily activities.

(2) Energy for movement, running, fighting and sleeping.

(3) Maintenance of body temperature, at about 39°C.

(4) Digestion of food, remembering that more energy will be required to digest the fibrous foods.

After these activities are met, then energy is available for production in the form of growth or reproduction. This may be lean-tissue growth, deposited as fat, or used to provide immediate energy.

ENERGY MEASUREMENTS

The total energy of the food before it is eaten is relatively easy to measure. This is known as the Gross Energy of the food, but it does not tell us a great deal about its feeding value. The gross energy of a feed can be measured by burning a given weighed sample in a bomb calorimeter in a laboratory. Energy was traditionally expressed in calories, but the term has now been replaced in animal nutrition by the joule. The joule is a very small unit and the nutritionists use one million joules—called megajoules (MJ)—as a working definition. For instance, 12,630,000 joules = 12·6 (MJ).

What we are really interested in is the Net Energy of the food, that is the food available to the pig for maintenance, growth and reproduction.

The route from the gross energy to net energy of a food could be shown in diagrammatic form as follows:

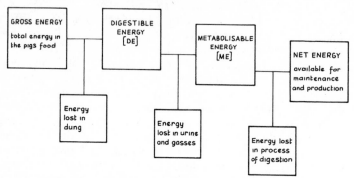

FIG. 34. *Route from gross energy to net energy of a food.*

Gross energy has already been described, and energy lost in the dung leaves the Digestible Energy (DE) of the food. Further energy loss is incurred through the urine losses, gases and 'wind', leaving us with Metabolisable Energy (ME). More energy will now be used in digestive and absorption processes and in keeping warm, and the balance remaining as net energy will be used for maintenance, growth and reproduction.

The use of the ME system is now used by nutritionists to measure and define the energy values—and hopefully—the value of food materials and formulated rations. Typical energy measurements for a range of pig feeds would now be shown as follows:

	MJ/Kg(DE)	MJ/Kg(ME)
Sow feed	12·73	12·15
Super creep	16·60	15·85
Grower feed	13·65	13·03
Finisher	12·92	12·32

PROTEINS AND AMINO ACIDS

Proteins are constructed from varying combinations of amino acids, and contain varying quantities of these individual amino acids.

Some amino acids are more important to the animal than others, eg, lysine, cystine and methionine are particularly important for pigs. Therefore, different kinds of protein are more valuable nutritionally than others, depending upon their contents of these vital amino acids. Generally speaking, animal proteins—meat meal, fish meal, milk powder—are good sources of lysine (the most important for pigs) and cereal and other vegetable proteins are poor sources.

Even though fish meal is generally high in lysine content, it may be that the use of too much heat during processing of the meal reduces the available amount of the amino acids. This is because the chemical structure of the protein is changed by the processing to such an extent that the pig cannot digest and absorb the essential lysine, and other amino acids that it contains. Feed conversion, lean meat production and maybe health will suffer according to the degree of damage—and there is a wide range of variation of availability.

Thus all ingredients are purchased and feed formulated on the basis of known total and available contents of the most important amino acids—lysine in particular.

PRACTICAL APPLICATION

A good example of the practical application or nutritional research can be illustrated with a brief reference to the density of pig diets. High Nutrient Density (HND) is a term we are hearing much more about in pig-feeding. The concept is not entirely new, as dairy farmers have long been used to feeding dairy cake at 1·8 or 1·6kg to 4·5 litres, and poultry and turkey rations have utilised this approach of packing more nutrient value into a particular package.

High density diet feeding is linked to a certain level of daily nutrient intake which provides the pig with a large number of essential nutrients. Daily nutrient intake can be altered by feeding more or less food, or altering the nutrient content of the food, or by a combination of both methods. Perhaps in the past there has been too much attention to nutrient content and make-up and not enough to the level of feeding.

It is possible to achieve the same nutrient intake by feeding different diets at different levels as shown in the table below.

Diet	Daily Feed Intake kg	Protein in Diet %	Daily Protein Intake kg	Energy of Diet MJ/kg(DE)	Daily Intake
Low Density	2·7	12·5	0·345	10·0	27·00
Medium Density	2·26	15·0	0·345	12·0	27·00
High Density	1·8	18·75	0·345	15·0	27·00

The task of the nutritionist is to provide the correct balance of energy, proteins—especially amino acids—vitamins and minerals after all maintenance requirements have been met. The feeder then has to feed the particular product at the correct level, taking into consideration the environmental conditions, the genetic potential, and the health status of the pig, as well as the end market.

These are some of the underlying principles in pig nutrition, and research and development continue into the nutrition of both the fattening and the breeding pig. Pigs appear to be highly tolerant of changes in the make-up and formulation of their balanced rations, which is fortunate as it leaves room for further exploration and improvements in pig nutrition.

Apart from lower feed costs, there are other arguments in favour of these diets. These include an improved killing-out percentage, where even a small improvement of $1–1\frac{1}{2}$ per cent will improve profit by 80–100p per pig. The fat or tallow used in manufacturing the feed also binds the food together and gives less dust and less wastage in the fattening house. Moreover, pigs on these diets have an improved skin condition, giving a distinctive 'bloomy' appearance which is quite remarkable even to the casual observer. The lower fibre content of the HND diet leads to direct energy saving in the digestive processes of the growing pig and a small bonus, that at the end of the digestive system there is less dung to push out and less to be dealt with in the slurry tank or the dung passage.

One final advantage from the pig farmer's angle is that he can feed one diet through from weaning to slaughter. Feed levels, or daily nutrient intake, can be varied by increasing daily food intake on a progressive basis according to requirement of the pigs and of the market outlet. The advantage for the compounder is that he is able to lower overhead costs, especially on labour, storage, and transport, which are major factors in the costs of production.

These less bulky, improved, high-energy foods require advanced manufacturing techniques and careful quality control. They are naturally more expensive in actual cost per tonne, but cost less in terms of pig meat produced per tonne of food fed. There are, however, certain points to be made about their use.

Field experience indicates that these foods perform best with certain strains of improved pigs, and it appears that there may be an interaction between improved genetic material and high-energy feeds. Research and field trials are being carried out to verify these findings. On a practical basis, it is quite clear that a high standard of environment and housing is essential to allow these diets to perform somewhere near their potential. Draught-free housing, and temperature about 20–22°C appear to be the optimum conditions, and the house temperature at pig level is critical.

One final point is that great precision is needed in determining feed levels and in accurately feeding these amounts. Obviously, over-feeding will lead to poor carcase quality, and wasteful feeding of a higher-cost food will increase, not lower, the total food cost, with the opposite effect on profits.

FOOD PREPARATION AND PURCHASE

On-the-farm decisions have to be taken about the method of buying pig food. In practice there are two possible solutions:

(1) Purchase of compounds.
(2) Preparation of food on the farm:
    (a) Use of cereals and a proprietary concentrate.
    (b) Use of straights and the mixture of a range of raw materials including proteins, minerals, and vitamins.
    (c) Mobile mixer for home-produced cereals and concentrate.

TABLE 16. Compound Food—Pigs
United Kingdom (million tonnes)

	'69	'70	'71	'72	'73	'74	'75	'76
Pig starters (milk equivalent type)	0·03	0·03	0·02	0·02	0·02	0·03	0·02	0·07
Balancers and concentrates	0·21	0·22	0·22	0·23	0·24	0·19	0·16	0·18
All other pig food	2·17	2·35	2·42	2·28	2·54	2·38	1·99	2·21
Total	2·41	2·60	2·66	2·53	2·80	2·60	2·17	2·46

Table 16 gives some indication of the recent trends in the production of compounds in the UK.

These figures clearly illustrate the cyclical nature of the pig industry and also show the steady growth from 1969 to a peak in 1973. The figures for 1975 reflect the low state of the industry at that time, with a reduction in pig numbers, followed by a slight increase in 1976. Trends for 1977 show a very similar picture to that of 1976.

One interesting figure is that of pig starters (milk equivalent type) for 1976. This probably reflects two main factors, which are the compulsory inclusion of surplus skim milk powder in pig rations as a result of the EEC 'milk powder mountain', and an increasing use of milk starter diets as a widespread result of earlier weaning.

Balancer and concentrate sales are shown under one category, but an analysis of this would show a reduction in balancer sales and increasing sales of concentrates. Usage of concentrates represents a large amount of actual pig feed when mixing rates are taken into account.

Feed Processing Machinery on Farms

Estimated numbers of feed-processing machines owned by occupiers of agricultural holdings at March 1969 (the latest year for which figures are available) compared with figures from previous census in 1965.

These figures refer to all farm feed-processing machinery but it is impossible to isolate trends for a particular species, in this case pigs. One significant feature is the increase of combined milling and mixing units by 26 per cent.

Many of these installations are completely automated and are often linked to the use of cubing machinery on the farm. This increase in the

E

TABLE 17. Feed Processing Machines on Farms (UK)

Type of machine		March 1965	1969	Difference %
Mills and crushers (single purpose)	Roller crushers Hammer mills and other grinding mills	33,740	37,750	+12
		58,160*	39,750	—32
Meal mixers		9,830	11,060	+13
Combined milling and mixing units		7,220†	9,110	+26
Cubers and pelleters		900	960	+ 6

* Collected in March 1965 as 'hammer mills, grinding and crushing mills, power operated (excluding roller crusher)'.
† Collected in March 1965 as 'completed grinding and mixing units'.
Source: MAFF.

use of on-farm cubing is again reflected in the figures, with an increase of 6 per cent over a four-year period (1965–1969).

Unfortunately no figures have been published for mobile feed-processing units, but a large number of these machines are operating throughout the country. This type of equipment was introduced into this country about 20 years ago from the USA. At first only meal could be produced on the farm, but more recently mobile mixers have been developed which are capable of cubing.

Feed compounders operate some of these machines to provide a useful outlet for their concentrates. Using the mobile mixer is a sort of 'halfway house' between farm processing and buying in compounds.

COMPOUNDS OR ON-FARM FOOD PREPARATION?

The tables give some indication of trends, but the final decision will depend upon many factors. A large arable farm with a pig enterprise, for instance, in grain-growing areas with home-produced cereals, storage and handling facilities, will almost certainly prepare pig food on the farm. A large intensive pig unit on limited acreage will generate a good deal of purchasing power and will forward buy in bulk, obtaining some healthy discounts.

Obviously these are straightforward cases, but where a change of policy is about to take place a number of points must be considered. Home-mixed rations will always show a 'face' value saving of between £2 to £4 per tonne, but straight price per tonne can be a misleading argument. Decisions should only be made after a thorough investigation of the financial implications. A businesslike budget study should be set up so that policies can be based on financial facts.

Some of the factors which should be considered include:

Capital
Is this best invested in machinery, equipment and staff or in livestock? Capital costs money in most cases. It has to be borrowed, interest paid, and security is usually demanded.

Siting, *layout and control*

Is power available? What about running repairs and maintenance? How near the point of feeding is food preparation? What about weighing, recording, and monitoring and analysis of raw materials?

Storage

Is this available and how many lines of raw materials are to be stocked? What about storage of finished rations?

Type of rations

Can we cater for all the categories of stock, and can we produce meal, nuts or pellets?. What about formulation and additives? Dust and shrinkage losses?

Labour

Will this usefully employ the extra staff involved on a full- or part-time basis? Reliability and job satisfaction for this critical job? Time spent buying, on the telephone for instance, and the cost of it—and who does the buying—and how good is your market intelligence?

Running costs

Labour, power, insurance, can be very high; automation will solve some of the problems but increases capital costs and depreciation.

Finally, it is generally agreed that there may be a large performance difference between the home-prepared food and compound rations, but, in spite of these arguments and counter-arguments, over 50 per cent of our pig feed is prepared on the farm and a large number of our pig farmers have made a considered decision on this point. This compares with 25 per cent of dairy farmers and under 20 per cent of poultry producers.

Certainly there is plenty of advice about balancing rations and inclusion rates for concentrates, much of this from the national feed firms who manufacture concentrates as well as their compounds. They recognise that there will be situations in which the compound feed is more profitable for the farmer and other cases where the concentrate is a better buy. Quite clearly there is a 'horses for courses' situation. Competition within the feed industry is very keen and it is in the long-term interest of the animal-feed compounder to be associated with profitable pig enterprises and a thriving pig industry.

One of the strong arguments recently advanced for the compounder has been his market knowledge and skill in buying, plus very advanced blending machinery which allows him to use a range of exotic ingredients likely to be available to us as a result of our having joined the EEC. Some forecasts indicate a move towards the Dutch pattern of almost entirely compound usage or the switch of German pig producers from home mixing to compounds. The outcome remains uncertain and on balance it seems that the British scene is unlikely to change dramatically.

We accept that compounds are the original 'instant pig feed' but there are other advantages, even if we have to pay for them. These include 'back-up' services such as advice on husbandry, marketing and recording. In some cases breed improvement has been originated by food compounders and a very large research and development effort has been directed at all aspects of pig improvement over the past 25 years. With changes in farm structure and with pressures inside the feed industry, advisory staff are much thinner on the ground than formerly: sales staff calling on the farm are, I think, much better trained, with a better knowledge of the pig industry. They are better informed by their parent companies, as much of the 'Magic and Mystique' of food preparation has disappeared, and at farm level more information is available on feed ingredients, energy levels, protein content, and its make-up. This, I think, is important and is a reflection of the changing standards and increasing efficiency being achieved in the pig industry.

SOW-FEEDING IN PRACTICE

Much basic research has been carried out into sow nutrition and feeding in the past few years, and an outline framework can be adopted for on-farm application. Precise recommendations will vary from farm to farm as breed, housing and management standards will differ. At the end of the day, we are aiming for the maximum number of weaners per sow at least food cost, or, to put it another way, sow productivity.

The important factors are:
(a) The farrowing index.
(b) The age at weaning.
(c) Number of pigs born.
(d) Number of pigs weaned.

The traditional approach to sow-feeding in this country tended towards over-feeding during pregnancy and under-feeding during lactation. Frequently these pregnancy and lactation periods were looked at in isolation, and large gains in sow bodyweight were made during pregnancy, only to be lost during lactation. These levels were based on 2·72–3·6kg per day during pregnancy with 4·0–4·98kg during lactation.

Work at a number of centres, including Nottingham University and the Rowett Institute, has shown that sow-feeding can be based on a lower feeding level during pregnancy and more generous feeding during lactation.

Feeding During Pregnancy

The following table summarises information from a trial carried out at the Rowett Institute and other co-ordinated centres. In these experiments three treatment levels were allocated over a period of three successive litters.

TABLE 18. Performance of Sows on Three Feed Levels

Treatment	*High*	*Medium*	*Low*
	kg	kg	kg
Feed intake per day	3·1	2·6	1·59
Liveweight gain of sow in pregnancy	69·3	48·6	26·55
Net gain in pregnancy	52·6	31·5	13·05
Birthweight of individual pigs (average)	1·45	1·36	1·68
Number in litter	11·0	11·1	10·7
Number of litters in experiment	116	113	123

The conclusions to be drawn from these experiments indicate that the level of feed intake during pregnancy had little or no effect upon the number of pigs born alive, the interval between weaning and service, or upon the health of the sow over a lifetime's performance. Clear relationships were established between feed intake, birth weight of the piglets, and liveweight changes in the sow, which were excessive in treatments on medium and high feed levels. Although heavy pigs at birth may be desirable, in economic terms it may not be worthwhile increasing pregnancy feed levels to achieve very high birth weights, especially if piglet protection, housing and management at farrowing and rearing are of a high standard.

Feed Intake in Lactation

Increasing feed intake during lactation will usually increase milk production. However, increased milk production will not necessarily lead to increase in piglet growth and weaning weight. Pigs or sows with poor milk performance will often compensate by increased intake of creep feed. The main benefit from increasing feed levels during lactation comes from the improved long-term performance on the body reserves of the sow. Repeated low feeding during lactation will probably affect subsequent pregnancies, birth weights of litters, and milk production in later lactations, as well as reproductive performance after weaning.

From this it appears that the assessment of sow productivity must be looked at from the overall performance of the sow over a number of litters, and one single way of achieving this is by monitoring weight changes of the sow from cycle to cycle. As a guide, it has been suggested that a good yardstick would be for sows to gain 10 to 15kg from one cycle to the next for the first four litters and to maintain their body-weight from cycle to cycle thereafter.

The best time at which to weigh is at service, as this will provide a point from which feed recommendations can be worked out to maintain a steady gain in sow condition. An example of this weight-gain cycle can be illustrated by a maiden gilt of 117kg at first service. After weaning her first litter, her target weight will be 131·5kg and by the time she has weaned her fourth litter she will have attained a bodyweight of 172·4kg, at which bodyweight should be stabilised. The amount of feed required to achieve this will vary according to housing, breed, and the nutritional level of the food, but practical recommendations can be worked out on a daily basis to come somewhere near the target.

SOW BODY WEIGHT CHANGES

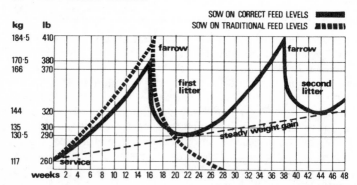

FIG. 35. *Diagram showing the correct weight gains over the sow's breeding life.*

This diagram illustrates the case of a gilt served at 117·0kg after first litter at about 131·5kg and after her second litter about 145kg, with the dotted line showing a steady bodyweight gain.

Sow-feeding—General Guidelines

As a general guide I am assuming the ration to be used will be one containing 15–16 per cent protein with an energy level of 13·0 DE (MJ/kg). Research has indicated that there may be a good case for feeding lower protein levels during parts of the pregnancy period, but that higher levels may be required at weaning and service and immediately afterwards, and perhaps for the last month of pregnancy. In lactation, feeding can be to appetite level, which will be about 4·5–5·4kg daily. This will depend on the size of the litter, environment and age at weaning.

The general health of the sow will also be an important consideration, as parasitic burdens allied to low-level feeding and poor housing may lead to a thin sow condition. Where lower levels of feeding are adopted, then individual feeding of sows is essential. During pregnancy once-daily feeding is acceptable, and a large number of pig farmers feed only once a day during lactation. In some cases during lactation, especially with first-litter sows, it may be necessary to feed twice daily to persuade them to maintain a sufficient daily feed intake. More specific recommendations for feeding at farrowing, weaning and service have been described in the section on management of the breeding sow (Chapter 6).

Feeding of the breeding herd can be summarised in table form, but emphasis is again placed on breed, housing, management, and health status of the herd.

TABLE 19. Feeding of the Breeding Herd

Animal	kg/day	Comments
Pregnant sow	1·8–2·26	Watch body weight and condition
Lactating sow	4·5–5·4	5 to 6 week weaning
Lactating sow	2·7–3·6	3 week or earlier weaning
Breeding boars	2·26–3·1	Age, size, and work rate
Gilts	1·8–2·26	Avoid over-fatness

NB: Where a high-energy food is used, then feeding levels may be reduced.

Creep-feeding

This is now a well-established practice which allows young pigs, whilst suckling, access to supplementary feed. It is particularly important with five- to six-week weaning and has a major effect on increasing the weight of the weaner pig, whilst helping to prevent excessive bodily weight losses in the sow. Sow milk output is normally about 6 to 8 litres per day. Yield increases up to a peak of about 10 to 12 litres in the third week of lactation, then gradually declines. Milk yield increases with the number of lactations and with the size of litter. Creep feed intake will increase as the sow's milk supply falls away.

The main qualities of a creep feed must be its palatability and digestibility. Formulation will include high energy and protein contents, with animal proteins such as fish meal and dried milk products. Feeds are in pellet or crumb form, and because the ration may contain emulsified fats, molasses, and flavouring, shelf life is relatively limited. Packaging and handling should help to keep the product fresh, and this is an important factor to remember on the farm. Creep-feeding calls for a well-designed product and skilful presentation to the pig. This is an integral part of litter management and will be described in that section. Quantities eaten will be in the region of 1·8 to 2·26kg per pig before weaning with five- to six-week weaning, and at that stage the intake will be about 0·45 to 0·68kg per day. Occasionally a starter creep of the sow milk-substitute type is used for three-week weaning.

Weaning at seven to ten days demands a special early-weaning diet which has been formulated for this purpose and for cage rearing. Palatability is exceptionally important, and carefully formulated milk products form the base of these rations. Vitamin and mineral levels are usually increased and quality control demands are very high in these specialist early-weaning diets.

FEEDING METHODS

Restricted or ad libitum?

There is a large amount of research work and practical experience on which to base recommendations in this field and the classical work carried out by Hammond and McMeekan in the late 1930s still holds good. Various experiments on planes of feeding showed quite clearly that the high/low feed levels gave the best carcases for our graded markets, which were based on Wiltshite-type cure. This work showed that growth and development of the pig began with vital organs, then bone and skeletal growth, followed by lean muscle, and finally by fat deposition. Certain breeds, such as the Middle White and Berkshire, which were early maturing, were unsuitable for the specialist bacon-curing trade as they tended to lay fat down at an early stage.

The Large White and Landrace, which provide the bulk of our national herd in purebred form and from their hybrid progeny, are late maturing and with many strains of these pigs it is still essential to restrict feed intake in the later stages of fattening to meet grading standards for pork, cutter and bacon.

The on-farm compromise for feeding this type of pig allows *ad lib* feeding until 36 to 45kg liveweight, followed by restriction on a daily basis to a fixed amount. Skill is needed to arrive at this daily figure and there will be a range of levels, depending on the genetic potential of the pig and the type and quality of the ration. The point at which feed restriction begins will be affected by the breed and type of pig. Continuous selection of some lines pinpoints some pigs that can be fed *ad lib* through to bacon weight without loss of carcase quality. *Ad lib* feeding will give a faster growth rate but at the expense of feed conversion ratio and food consumption, whilst it is clearly a labour-saving operation as hoppers can be serviced on an infrequent basis to fit in with work routine. However, over-restriction can lead to a situation where a disproportionate amount of food is used for maintenance rather than production, with adverse effects on feed-conversion rates.

Some market outlets allow *ad lib* feeding to be used to slaughter weight. These include the manufacturing pig and the ungraded cutter. A cheap cereal-based farm ration will be the usual choice of feed, but even then a check should be made on food intakes and food conversion rate, which may become excessive.

TABLE 20. Comparison of Pigs—ad lib v Restricted Feeding

Effect of ad lib feeding	Growth rate	Feed/gain ratio	Carcase quality
Improvement	88	13	1
Deterioration	—	60	72
None	1	12	10
No information available	—	4	6

Source: Braude 1972.

The pattern of *ad lib* feeding followed by restriction is widely used in commercial pig farming. This not only follows practical research findings but fits in with housing and management systems that group the young pigs at weaning before drawing out pens of pigs for final fattening.

As indicated, a system has to be worked out in each farm situation which balances throughput, housing systems, labour requirements, and performance in terms of carcase quality and food-conversion efficiency. This also needs to be considered against the background of the nutritive value of the rations being fed.

Sex Differences and Feeding Levels

One very practical recommendation for improving carcase quality for the bacon market can be followed if castrates and gilts are separated during fattening. The table illustrates the interaction between sex and carcase quality.

TABLE 21. Effect of Sex on Growth and development of Progeny-tested Pigs

| Performance | Large White | |
22–90kg Liveweight	Castrates	Gilts
DLWG (kg)	0·67	0·67
FCE	3·26	3·16
Carcase length (mm)	804	809
C (mm)	21	17
Shoulder fat (mm)	32·1	32·1
Lean in carcase (%)	51·8	55·8

Source: Cuthbertson and Pease 1968.

Quite clearly, gilts use their feed more efficiently than the hogs, and produce a leaner carcase. In practice the sexes can be separated when food restriction takes place at 36 to 45kg liveweight. Some farmers will choose to send hogs for a different market—pork or cutter—or control feed levels more carefully. At the same time, it would be possible to increase feed levels of gilts by up to 0·23kg of food per day without loss of carcase quality, thus increasing throughput of fattening pigs.

Frequency of Feeding

Fortunately there are some experimental results to act as guidelines for commercial practice. There is no advantage in more than twice-daily feeding and once daily is quite acceptable, providing the trough space is sufficient and water is available at all times. Omission of feeds at weekends, for instance, is permissible as long as this is compensated for in the total weekly amount. Growth, food-conversion ratio, and carcase quality were not adversely affected in feed trials, but it is emphasised that feeds omitted must be redistributed among the reduced number of feeds per week.

In most cases, twice-daily feeding is the correct choice, but where mechanical dry-feeding systems are installed there may be management reasons for feeding three to four times a day.

Wet or Dry?

The general conclusion from a very large number of world-wide experiments must be that wet feeding results in a better performance. The following table summarises the evidence.

TABLE 22. Comparison of Performance of Pigs on Wet or Dry Feeding
(54 experiments reported)

Effect of wet feeding	Growth rate	Feed/gain ratio	Carcase quality
Improvement	29	25	6
Deterioration	3	4	1
None	12	15	16
No information available	—	—	21

Source: Braude 1972.

Quite simply, there is a marked improvement in growth rate and feeding efficiency, but the evidence on carcase quality is not so clear.

A trial co-ordinated in this country by Dr Braude with 19 participating centres gave the following results.

TABLE 23. Comparison of Performance of Pigs on Dry Meal and Wet Mix

	FCR start to 54kg	FCR 54 to 90kg	FCR overall
Dry meal, troughs	3·10	4·01	3·59
Wet mix	2·96	3·75	3·34

This trial also used different ratios of meal to water, as the following table shows:

TABLE 24. Trial Using Different Ratios of Water to Meal

Ratio water to meal	4:1	2½:1	1½:1	Dry meal
Extra water	Nil	Nil	ad lib	ad lib
Growth rate, kg/day	0·59	0·61	0·60	0·57
Feed conversion rate	3·45	3·36	3·34	3·59

The conclusion from these trials shows that both improved food conversion and growth rate can be obtained with wet feeding without loss of carcase quality.

Meal or Pellets?

Further work on the ARC trials compared wet feeding with meal or pellets with the following results.

TABLE 25. Feed Conversion Efficiency

	Start to 54kg	54kg to slaughter	Overall
Dry meal trough	3·10	4·01	3·58
Dry meal floor	3·27	4·22	3·76
Pellets trough	3·071	3·95	3·52
Pellets floor	3·079	3·98	3·53
Wet mix	2·96	3·75	3·3

On this basis wet feeding was the best system, followed by pellets on the floor or in the trough. Saving on food is considerable, as the following table shows—with wet feeding saving approximately 9kg of food per pig, worth about 80p per pig at the present time.

TABLE 26. Feeding Comparison—Meal, Cubes and Wet Mix

	Start to 54kg		54kg to slaughter	
	Improved conversion rate	Food savings per pig kg	Improved conversion rate	Food savings per pig kg
(Dry meal in troughs)				
Dry meal on floor	0·104	—3·32	—0·210	—7·56
Cubes in trough	0·099	3·1	0·058	2·04
Cubes on floor	0·091	2·9	0·026	0·9
Wet mix	0·147	4·73	0·260	9·7

When comparing meal with pellets the overall evidence points to a superior performance of pigs fed pellets, nuts or cubes over pigs fed on meal.

TABLE 27. Comparison of Performance of Pigs Fed Pellets or Meal
(57 experiments)

Effect of pellets	Growth rate	Fede/gain ratio
Improvement	39	48
Deterioration	2	1
None	16	7
No information available	—	1

Source: Braude 1972.

From all this information the following general conclusions can be drawn:

    (a) Pigs fed *ad lib* grow faster, utilise their feed less efficiently, and produce fatter, lower-quality carcases than those on restricted systems.

    (b) There is no advantage in feeding more than twice daily.

    (c) When comparing wet and dry feeding systems, wet feeding gives better results.

    (d) A comparison of pigs fed pellets with pigs fed on meal indicates a superior performance from pellet feeding.

In practical terms, where meal is to be fed, then it should be wet fed, otherwise pellets, cubes or nuts are the best alternative.

FEEDING THE MEAT PIG FOR GRADED MARKET OUTLETS

Feed recommendations for the pig after weaning can only be a general guide, as they will depend on several factors, including:

    (1) The genetic potential of the pig.

    (2) The housing and environment.

    (3) The nutrient value of the food.

    (4) The specific outlet the pig is intended for.

Market Outlets

At the present time (1981) these can be summarised as follows:

TABLE 28. Market Outlets by Live and Dead Weight

Type of pig	Liveweight kg	Deadweight kg	Killing out %
Light pork	54–59·5	40·5–45	70–72
Heavy pork	59·5–67·6	45–49·5	71–73
Cutter	72–81	54–59·9	72–74
Bacon	85–94·5	61·76–67·6	73–76
Manufacturing	117–126	61·76–67·6	77–82

Killing-out Percentage

This is expressed as the dressed weight of the cold carcase as a ratio of the liveweight of the animal.

$$\frac{\text{Carcase weight} \times 100}{\text{Liveweight}} = \text{Killing out } \%$$

This ratio will be affected by the weight of the animal at slaughter as the table shows, and the heavier the pig the better the killing-out percentage. This increase in KO percentage with the older and heavier animal is because internal organs form a progressively smaller proportion of the total weight of the animal in relation to the muscle, fat and bone content. Pre-slaughter treatment, such as transport, feeding and watering procedures immediately before slaughter will affect the killing-out percentage, with fasted pigs giving a higher figure.

Feeding methods will also make a difference. Pigs fed bulky foods with high fibre content will have larger gut and intestine and a lower killing-out percentage than pigs fed on low fibre, high-energy feeds. Figures may vary by 3 to 5 per cent which will show a considerable difference in returns. For example, a 90kg liveweight pig killing-out at 71 per cent will give a carcase weight of 64·4kg, but if the killing-out percentage is 75 per cent—a likely result with high-density rations— then there will be a carcase weight of 68kg. Thus 3·6kg difference at 70p/kg is worth £2·52 to the producer. Not all of it will be extra profit as the higher cost of feed will have to be allowed for, but it is a worthwhile return.

Carcase Quality—and Some Ways of Measuring It

The carcase quality of the pig is now assessed by some reasonably simple measurements. Weight is important, as some market outlets specify a certain weight range. Length is also important for bacon pigs for the Wiltshire cure, but most pigs now satisfy the minimum requirements in this respect.

Most methods of carcase classification assess the amount of lean meat present, and payment is made on the basis with a series of grades worked out which financially penalise the poorer carcases. Other carcase characteristics less easy to quantify include shape and conformation, and the colour, texture and flavour of the meat.

Most carcases are measured on the thickness of backfat present at specific points on the shoulder and loin. Length is measured from the anterior edge of the aitch bone to the anterior edge of the first rib. More recently an instrument called the intrascope or optical probe has been developed, which will measure the thickness of fat over the eye muscle at a point known as P_2.

The probe can be used on split or unsplit carcases, and measurements can be taken at a series of points to give a very good indication of the lean-to-fat ratio. This is linked to payment grades and many bacon, pork or cutter pigs are now graded by this method and contracts drawn up on this basis.

Bacon pigs

A probe measurement of backfat thickness is taken at 6·5cm (P_2) from the midline of the back at the last rib, and this measurement, together with measurements of visible backfat at the shoulder and loin, indicates the degree of fatness.

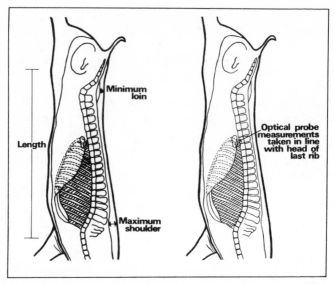

FIG. 36. *(Left) Points at which carcase measurements are taken. (Right) Split carcase measurements.*

Pork, cutter and manufacturing pig

Backfat measurements are taken in millimetres with an optical probe (intrascope) at two fixed points over the loin—4·5cm (P_1) and 8cm (P_3) from the midline of the back at the last rib. The measurements are added together to describe the degree of fatness.

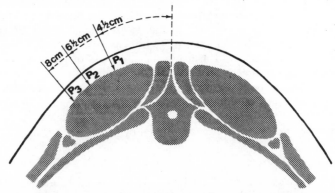

FIG. 37. *Position of measurements taken with an optical probe (intrascope) at the level of the head of the last rib. P_1 and P_3 apply to split or unsplit carcases and P_2 to split carcases.*

Bacon Pigs—Typical Wiltshire Contract

This extract from a bacon contract shows exactly the weight ranges and measurements that have to be obtained to qualify for the different grades. Payment is then made on a quality basis which encourages the production of lean meat for this particular market.

TABLE 29. Bacon Pigs—Typical Wiltshire Contract.
Grading Measurements of Clean Pigs from 59kg to 77kg Deadweight

Grade	Weight	Length (minimum)	Backfat Shoulder/ Loin (maximum)	P_2 Probe Measurement (maximum)
A1	61kg to 70kg*†	775mm	42/22mm	20mm
B1	61kg to 70kg*†	775mm	45/25mm	20mm
	61kg to 70kg*†	—	42/22mm	22mm
2	61kg to 70kg*	775mm	48/28mm	22mm
	61kg to 70kg*	775mm	45/25mm	24mm
	61kg to 70kg*	—	45/25mm	22mm
	73kg to 77kg	775mm	45/25mm	22mm
C	59kg to 77kg	Other pigs not falling in the above grades		

* *Pigs with grade A1, B1 and or 2 measurements weighing between 70·5kg and 72·5kg inclusive will be paid for at the amount payable for a pig weighing 70kg at the grade A1, B1 or 2 as the case may be.*
† *Pigs with grade A1, or B1 measurements weighing between 59kg and 60·5kg inclusive will be paid for at the amount payable for a pig weighing 59kg at the grade A1 or B1 as the case may be.*

NOTES:
In the case of pigs graded 'skin-off', the backfat and P_2 probe measurements will be 5mm less than the above.
The P_2 probe measurements will be taken at the last rib 6·5cm from the centre line of the carcase and will be taken on the day of slaughter except in the case of pigs graded with 'skin-off' when such measurement will be taken not later than the day following the day of slaughter.
The loin measurement will relate to the thickness of fat over the top of the rump muscle.
The shoulder measurement will relate to the thickness of fat on the shoulder at the fattest part.
The length measurement shall be taken from the indentation of the first rib to the anterior edge of the aitch bone.
The above measurements (other than that for weight) shall apply whether the carcase is hot or cold.

Factors Affecting Carcase Quality

Some of these factors have already been discussed and are dealt with in various parts of the section on feeding the meat pigs. These factors can be summarised under the following headings.

(a) Breeding.
(b) Nutrition and feeding.
(c) Age and weight at slaughter.
(d) Housing and environment.
(e) Sex difference.

The profitability of the pig-fattening enterprise is largely dependent on the ability to operate within a framework of breed and environment and to balance these factors with the best food fed at the right level for these graded market outlets. Boar meat production is discussed in Chapter 12.

The Grower Pig

As a guide, the grower pig will be considered in the weight range from 11·34 to 36kg. A change will be made from creep feed to grower rations either just before or after weaning. With six-week weaning the change will already have been made, with earlier weaning the creep feed may be carried through to the post-weaning period. *Ad lib* feeding will be the usual method, using fixed hoppers with feed available at all times. There will be less waste if pellets are used, and, as discussed earlier, a slightly better performance than with meal.

The point at which restriction is imposed will depend again on the genetic potential of the pig and choice of market outlet.

An on-farm system can be simply arrived at with a few well-run trials. As a guide, pork pigs can be fed *ad lib* safely to 31 to 33·2kg liveweight, cutter and bacon pigs to 36·2 to 40·8kg, and a balance must be achieved between food intake, carcase quality and throughput. In some cases, farmers will prefer to restrict feed levels from weaning on a daily appetite basis until a maximum daily intake is arrived at, when controlled restriction begins.

Pigs destined for manufacturing outlets can be fed *ad lib* right through to slaughter weight, although there may be a change from higher to lower protein ration at about 45–54kg liveweight mark.

Management aspects of this stage of pig production will be enlarged upon in a later section, with some recommendations for feeder space, and frequency of servicing hoppers and feeders.

Pork, Cutter and Bacon

As a general guide, all feeding pigs for graded outlets can be fed on a similar restricted scale, with the lighter pigs for pork and cutter being sent for slaughter at a lower point on the selected scale. Feeding levels will vary on each farm and an on-farm solution must be worked out according to breed, environment and feed quality.

Twice-daily feeding is the usual practice but once daily is acceptable. Recent work at Wye College suggests that quantities could be worked out on a weekly or fortnightly basis, and precise daily weighing out of feed quantities may not be necessary. I emphasise, however, that the total food amount still needs to be accurately assessed. Traditionally, feeding scales were worked out from a base of about 1kg at a weaning weight of 13·6 to 18kg with a weekly increment of 0·11kg per pig.

Other scales were worked out on a weight basis and were slightly more generous. The following table gives some traditional typical examples:

TABLE 30. Feeding Scales

A			B			C	
Wt in kg	kg Daily		Wt in kg	kg Daily		Weeks	kg Daily
13·6	0·68		13·6	0·9		6	0·68
18	0·79						
22·6	0·9	or	22·6	1·13	or	8	0·9
27	1·01	ad lib			ad lib		
31	1·13		31	1·36		10	1·13
36	1·24					12	1·36
40	1·36		40	1·59		14	1·59
						16	1·70
45	1·47		49·5	1·8		18	1·8
54	1·59	Pork	59·5	1·91	Pork	20	2·04
63	1·70		67·6	2·04			
72	1·91					22	2·15
76	2·04		72·1	2·15		24	2·26
81	2·15					26	2·49
85	2·26		85	2·26			
90	2·37	Bacon	94·5	2·49	Bacon		

These scales would be suitable for a medium-density feed with good housing conditions and pigs that need modest restriction as they approach bacon weight. Brief trials would quickly establish the most profitable feed levels.

With the use of high-energy feeds a quite different scale can be worked out, and the following table gives some indication of feed recommendations and performance standards to be expected.

TABLE 31. High Energy Feed—One Diet

Liveweight pigs	kg per day	Week	Gain per week	FCR
kg	kg		kg	
13·6–18	0·90	14	3·1–4	1·8
20·26–24·6	1·13	17½	3·6–4·5	1·9
27–36	1·36	21	3·6–4·95	2·0
36–45	1·475	24½	4·0–	2·1
45–63	1·59	24½	4·0–5·86	2·5
63–90	1·705	26¼	4·5–6·3	2·6

These figures apply to carefully selected strains of hybrid pigs, with precise food control, well-insulated housing and good management.

Manufacturing Pigs

Probably the simplest of pigs to feed with a system based on home-produced cereals plus a concentrate. Where dry feeding is used, a two-stage ration is used, but feed efficiency falls off rapidly after 90kg liveweight. *Ad lib* feeding is often the preferred method, though occasionally wet feeding is used and pigs can be restricted to appetite levels, with an improvement in feed conversion and an overall saving in food costs.

Feeding—Measures of Efficiency

Some definitions of the terms currently used to measure food usage include the following:

Food Conversion Efficiency or Ratio (FCE or FCR)

The number of kilograms of food required to increase the liveweight of the pig by one kilogram, usually measured over a given period of time. This is a rather crude measure, as it does not take into account the nutrient value or cost of the food used. Feed efficiency will fall off as the pig increases in size, and variations will occur between strains of pigs. Also feed efficiency is particularly sensitive to environmental and housing conditions. As indicated earlier, a wide range of performance figures are recorded but an improvement of 0·2—for example from 3·3 down to 3·1—will at present feed prices save about 13·0kg of feed, or about £1·30 per pig.

Cost per kg Liveweight Gain

Another measure that can be used in pig-meat production is cost of liveweight gain. This combines the cost of the food and the efficiency with which it is used by the pig. This combined figure is a better guide to economic production than FCE used on its own.

TABLE 32. Food Conversion Ratio

Cost of food (£ per tonne)	2·4	2·6	2·8	3·0	3·2	3·4	3·6
80	19·3	20·8	22·4	24·0	25·5	27·1	29·0
90	21·6	23·4	25·2	27·0	28·8	30·6	32·4
100	24·0	26·0	28·0	30·0	32·0	34·0	36·0
110	26·4	28·6	30·8	33·0	35·2	37·4	39·6
120	28·8	31·2	33·6	36·0	38·4	40·8	43·2
130	31·2	33·8	36·4	39·0	41·6	44·2	46·8

This table shows that feed cost per kg liveweight gain of 6p can be achieved by either a food cost of £100 tonne at 3·6 food conversion ratio or feed at £120 per tonne and at food conversion of 3·0.

Cost per kg Deadweight

A further refinement takes into account killing-out percentage so that we can compare FCE and cost per kg LWG. As most pigs are sold deadweight, different types and weights of pig can be compared on a similar basis. The percentage of lean meat can be accurately determined, then we can get down to cost per kg of lean meat produced. This is probably as far as we need to go in determining the different costs of production between various types and weights of pigs.

MECHANICAL FEEDING

As pig units have grown in size there has been increasing interest in mechanical feeding. Slop feeding has been a traditional part of pig feeding for many years, and the cottager's sty was fitted with a trough for that purpose. Mechanised pipeline feeding began in the 1950s and a well-tried engineering principle is used for conveying the feed by centrifugal pump and a 50·0mm pipeline for metered delivery to the pigs' trough on a twice-daily basis.

Mechanical dry feeding originated in the States and in Europe, where considerable emphasis is placed upon labour-saving techniques. Meal or pellets can be conveyed and dispensed with great accuracy. Obviously, any form of mechanical feeding will increase the capital cost of the pig enterprise, but with labour costs increasing it makes sense to release labour from physical drudgery and allow more time for inspection, observation and stockmanship.

Pipeline feeding

If we consider some of the advantages and disadvantages of pipeline feeding systems, a table can be drawn up as follows:

Advantages	Disadvantages
Improved performance over dry meal feeding in feed conversion and liveweight gain.	Accurate quantitative distribution will increase capital costs, especially with automatic valves.
Reduction of waste and less dust.	Blockages will occur in pipelines and valves.
Labour saving and convenience.	Pipelines may freeze.
Adaptable for existing or unconventional layouts.	One ration only, so confined to one class of stock.
Built-in mixer for concentrates and straights.	Increase in slurry problems and a tendency for pipeline-fed pigs to lie wet as more urine is produced.
Can be used for wide range of products including swill, skim milk, whey and vegetables.	House layout linked to trough design—higher capital cost. Fineness of grinding of meal is critical for some systems, and may slow up mill output.

Wet-feeding systems—main categories

Batch-type mixers with mixing by rotating paddles or compressed air.
Continuous-sequence mixers with simultaneous mixing and dispensing of food.

Mobile mixer with mechanical mixer and portable tanker.

Early models were based on an underground tank with paddle-wheel agitators, with ingredients fed into the mixer with the help of gravity. Later models included above-ground plastic and steel tanks which required food to be augered in. In some cases mixing and delivery takes place by compressed air, which reduces HP requirements.

Pipelines—two main systems

(a) Ring circuits.
(b) Deadend or stop-end circuits.

Ring circuits

The ring pipeline requires more pipeline than the deadend system. Pipes, however, can be flushed and cleaned out by recirculating water. A better and more consistent mix can be obtained with this method by circulating food before feeding actually starts.

Deadend pipelines

Cheaper to install than ring circuits and when compressed air is used for distribution the pipeline can be cleaned and left empty, with less likelihood of frost damage.

Distribution in Troughs

The food is conveyed along 50·0mm pipelines at a dilution rate of about three parts of meal to one part of water. This consistency is about right for the pigs and is capable of being pumped around the circuit by centrifugal pump or compressed air. Branch pipes lead away from the main line and distribute food through a 'Tee' or 'Vee' piece to spread the feed along the trough. Quantitative distribution is achieved by a valve which should be sited as near the main line as possible. The valves which control the flow and feed are frequently hand operated.

Automatic valves, which will add to capital cost, are usually operated by a compressed-air system linked to a control box on which food levels can be accurately metered on a pen basis. Manual control of valves tends to be rather hit and miss. Stop watches and flashing lights can be used, but in the end accurate feeding depends on the judgement of the stockman operating the valve. Trough space requirements per pig are about 229 to 305mm with a half-round salt-glazed or plastic-faced trough giving the best answer.

Wet mixing and pipeline feeding have obviously an important place in pig-feeding systems. Without doubt they are best suited to those farms which produce their own cereals and have on-farm grain storage facilities. Quite often these can be linked to general-purpose Suffolk-type building with straw bedding and tractor scraping of manure. This is a natural integration of farm resources that will give good results without demanding very specialist management skills.

Mechanical Dry-feeding Systems

One feature of intensive pig systems is that they are often divorced from cereal-producing farms. In this case they rely heavily upon the purchase of compounds which are often bought in bulk in nut or pellet form. These are the ideal circumstances for mechanised feeding during fattening—from 27 to 90kg liveweight. Mechanised dry feeding is at present the growth area in pig equipment, and a wide range of feeders are being introduced into this country from Europe and the USA. A table can be drawn up which summarises points for and against as follows:

Advantages	*Disadvantages*
Meal or pellets can bed fed, on floor or in troughs.	Dust, especially with meal feeding.
Great accuracy of feeding levels.	Large number of moving parts to service.
Floor feeding gives saving in pig space allowances and gives flexibility in house design and layout.	Not easily extended to other buildings on expansion.

Dry Feeders—Classification

(a) Overhead feeders with dump-box dispensers.
(2) Mobile feeders on fixed tracks.

Overhead Feeders

A wide range of equipment has been devised on this basis. Dispensers are sited over each pen and are filled by conveyor systems. There are several choices, including endless-chain and flight, auger or pneumatic conveying, all linked on a circuit to the bulk-food supply. Auger systems are usually the most rapid; pneumatic systems may cause some food separation. Some conveying systems are unable to cope with a pellet size over 10mm, so watch this point.

The dispensers can be set at predetermined levels and measure volumetrically or by weight. Calibration is necessary if food varies in density. As pigs are pulled out for slaughter then adjustments are needed. Food can be released automatically, but in some cases the dispensers are operated by hand. With meal there may be a dust problem, but with pellets this problem is reduced and a good spread is obtained with floor feeding.

Once feeding has taken place, the conveyor comes into action again to refill the dispensers. A fail-safe system is essential to prevent the base of one dispenser remaining open and subsequent dislocation of the whole system.

Mobile Feeders

A variety of feeders exist, including a mobile hopper which travels on an overhead rail. Operation can be automatic or manual. Food is dispensed on to the floor by a calibrated auger which delivers a pre-set amount to each pen. In some cases these hoppers may have two arms and move down the centre of the house, metering food to each pen as they move along. Other mobile hoppers are designed for trough feeding and dispense feed down the house, activated by a time switch and calibrated system.

Other Dry Feeders

Trickle feeders are a combination of chain and flight conveyors in a metal trough suspended over the pen. Feed is trickled on to the floor through a series of adjustable perforations in the base of the metal trough. The number and size of these perforations can be controlled to adjust food levels.

Fixed feed hoppers can also be serviced by a wide variety of conveyors, though pneumatic and auger systems are most widely used. Farmers are, of course, very ingenious in designing and building their own mechanical feeding system, whether wet or dry, and a whole range of equipment and methods has been developed for mechanical feeding.

Finally, some general principles should be followed in selecting any mechanical pig-feeding system. These are:

Reliability

This is a first essential, as any delay or breakdown will create stress and play havoc with stock and stockman.

Waste Saving

Conveying and dispensing systems should eliminate waste from dust, inaccurate metering and over-feeding.

Fail-safe Design and Power-failure Alternatives

In the event of breakdown, a warning system should be triggered off so that action can be taken. In the event of a power failure, it should still be possible to feed the pigs by hand.

Extension and Flexibility

Mechanical feeding systems should be capable of extension as the unit grows in size, as it inevitably will.

Quality Control

With graded market outlets, it is of paramount importance to have an easily adjustable method of regulating the amount of food fed per pen. The design should also allow pens to be by-passed when they are not in use.

FEEDING BY HAND

It should not be overlooked that in some houses and with smaller herds feeding by hand may still be the best solution. Once- or twice-daily feeding can be well organised with a suitable layout and some simple work study. Careful siting of the food store, delivery points and bulk bins and the use of a wheeled feed truck can be as effective as many mechanical-feeding layouts. At least pigs will be seen at feeding time and action can be taken immediately to sort out the management and husbandry problems that happen on a daily basis.

Chapter 8

MANAGEMENT—Stock

MANAGEMENT PLAYS a key role in pig production by controlling other input factors. A definition I heard recently illustrated the art of management by referring to the baking of a cake. For this one needs an oven, a recipe and the right ingredients, but unless the management of the timing and temperature of the oven is correct the result can be complete failure, however good the ingredients and the recipe.

The Oxford dictionary is slightly more conventional and uses phrases such as 'skilful handling—to conduct the working of—to have effective control'. This last phrase is probably nearest the modern meaning of the word in pig-farming terms. Management is certainly an art and cannot be easily taught, but is a special blend of skill and experience. Recognition of what are normal situations, and the departure from those situations, is an essential part of management, especially with animals.

A major part of management under intensive livestock conditions is basic stockmanship. This has been defined as 'the instant and perceptive sympathy with the needs and requirements of the animal'.

We are slowly beginning to build up a method of pig management which can be quantified on the lines of industrial management, and vital areas and key tasks can be isolated in drawing up a management plan for any farm and situation. Management is also about men and their motivation, and I believe that staff welcome specific responsibility with detailed planning and organisation. I intend to spell out management and husbandry tasks at particular times through the various stages of pig production in some detail. At a later stage I will suggest daily and weekly routines as well as some outline job specifications that may prove a guide for large-scale pig units.

THE FARROWING SOW

Pre-farrowing

The sow should be settled into a warm, dry pen a few days before she is due to farrow. A dry floor is perhaps more important than a recently scrubbed, washed and disinfected, but wet, pen. Dry soft-wood shavings are the best choice of bedding material as they will not entangle the new-born pig as long straw does. Hygiene is important, but farrowing rooms will not always require resting and disinfection between each batch. The amount of cleaning and resting will depend upon the health of the herd, and three or four times a year should be sufficient.

Slatted and partially slatted floors should be thoroughly dried out and checked for any damage to the surface or any projections that might have appeared. A scattering of sawdust on the slat will add a little comfort for the sow.

A batch of sows that are to farrow within a 48-hour period should be brought into the farrowing room at the same time. As they are brought in, they should be well washed down, using a soft soap and warm water, to which should be added a mange and parasitic wash. This is also a good time to inspect teats and udder, and after washing the sow needs careful drying down. Washing the sow may in fact be more important than excessive washing of her farrowing quarters. A crate will normally be used for farrowing, and lamps and heaters should be checked for operation and safety.

When the sow moves into the farrowing house she should be fed a laxative diet for a few days to prevent constipation, and her total food intake should be reduced to prevent udder congestion, which pre-disposes to complications at farrowing. Careful handling and treatment of sows and gilts at this stage is important, and a few minutes spent stroking backs, handling udders, and 'chatting up' sows is time well spent.

At Farrowing

The restless signs of imminent parturition are well known, and a few hours before farrowing milk can be drawn from the teats. Most farrowings occur in the evening and the sow is quite capable of getting on with it herself quite quickly, providing she is in a crate with the correct room and creep temperature. Some stockmen prefer to cover slatted floors immediately behind the sow with a paper bag or a special wooden board, and this is a good idea.

Most staff will check their sows late at night, and if a sow is farrowing they will stay with her for a short time. Usually sows will farrow quickly with only a few minutes between each pig, and these are followed by the afterbirth so that the whole process might be over in a few hours. Prolonged intervals between pigs means that something is going wrong, and this may need veterinary attention or expert manipulation by a skilled stockman. Brief training and experience will indicate when interference is necessary, but this will be very rarely. Older, overweight or nervous sows will always give more problems at farrowing.

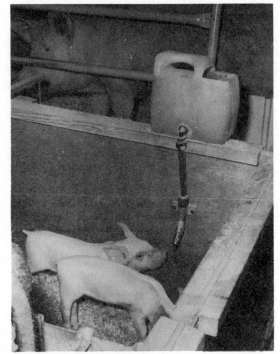

17. Farmer-designed watering arrangements for litters in creep area and farrowing pen.

18. A small creep feeder is essential to get creep-feeding under way.

19. General view of group suckling yards for six sows and litters.

20. A generous area is needed for the creep in group suckling yards.

21. Straw-based weaner pool developed at the NAC pig unit.

22. Internal view of verandah-type weaner house.

23. View of outer run of weaner verandah house.

24. A view of an outdoor weaner unit with slatted floors; slurry storage lagoons are in the background.

Pig Breeders Supply Co. photo

25. General view of Trobridge fattening layout.   *Pig Breeders Supply Co. photo*

26. Trobridge pen showing partially slatted floor.

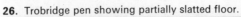

27. Internal view of Trobridge pen with solid floors and straw bedding.

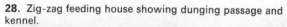

28. Zig-zag feeding house showing dunging passage and kennel.

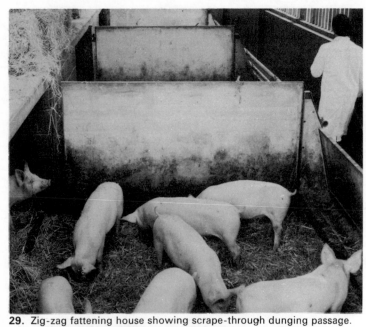

29. Zig-zag fattening house showing scrape-through dunging passage.

30. Automatic pipeline feeding in Suffolk-type fattening house.

31. Controlled-ventilation house showing ridge inlet with extraction fans on side walls.

32. Controlled-ventilation house—internal view showing open-pen layout and floor-feeding equipment. *NPD photo*

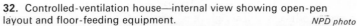

F

At birth the young pigs may need drying off and placing under the heater, and occasionally pigs are born wrapped in the afterbirth, or apparently stillborn at the end of a large litter or after prolonged farrowing. If someone is present these pigs can usually be saved by resuscitation, especially if the mouth and nostrils are cleared of obstruction.

Where sows farrow on their own, special attention must be paid to heaters, and a lamp placed safely immediately behind the sow for a few hours overnight can often save a pig. Navel cords will wither off, but extra long ones can be trimmed so that they don't wrap around legs and snouts.

Young pigs are born with eight very strong, sharp eye teeth, four on each jaw, and these should be clipped out as soon as possible after farrowing, otherwise they cause damage to the sow's udder and to each others' snouts and heads. A set of specially manufactured pliers can be used for this job. In some cases sows, and more especially gilts, become so uncomfortable because of these needle-sharp teeth that they refuse to allow the litter to suckle, which may lead to udder complications.

Where pigs are to be reared in intensive fattening houses tails will need docking. I find this is best done at birth, and in my experience only the end portion, in fact the top of the tail, needs to be docked. A spray with an antispetic should follow the operation.

Some producers will weigh pigs individually at birth, but total litter weight is a better figure to record. Weighing at birth is not essential but it gives some indication of successful sow feeding, and a heavier pig at birth usually has a better chance of survival. Spot checks on birth weights from time to time are probably the best solution.

Post Farrowing

Young pigs will quickly suckle by themselves, but the weaker, smaller pig can be encouraged by holding it to a teat for a few minutes. During farrowing the sow will be letting down her milk almost all the time. It is vital that the young pig receives some of this 'first milk' or colostrum, which contains antibodies which build up resistance to disease in the young pig. This is a good time when batch farrowing to balance-up litters by switching pigs and levelling up numbers.

After about 48 hours the litter will establish a teat order to which they will stick throughout suckling, with the front teats usually giving more milk. Milk let down will occur perhaps 12 to 15 times a day for the first few days after farrowing, gradually reducing in frequency. During this first suckling period a close watch must be kept on the sow's udder, and daily inspection by feeling with the hand will soon detect if any hardness or lumpiness is forming.

The behaviour of the litter will soon show whether everything is in order or not. They should 'fill out' quite quickly, and after suckling settle down under their lamp. If there is any shortage of milk, they will be generally uneasy and scrabbling for teats. These signs, along with udder hardness, indicate a metritis/mastitis complex, and veterinary attention will be required. If these infections are caught in good time response to antibiotic treatment can be fairly rapid.

Sow-feeding appears to be a critical factor in helping prevent this problem. Feeding should be based on a low-level laxative diet for a few days before and after farrowing, with twice-daily feeding, and a close watch should be kept on the sow to see that she dungs and urinates normally. Reluctance to eat may be the first indication that immediate post-farrowing complications are about to set in.

One practical tip that will help the litter to survive during a milk crisis is to provide a small amount of aired water in a gallon cube drinker. This will need changing several times in the day, as cleanliness is vital. A little glucose in the water may tempt the young pigs to drink and by doing so prevent dehydration. This treatment can often save litters, providing prompt veterinary action is given to the sow and her milk returns to normal within 48 hours.

Usually lactation will continue normally and sow-feed levels can be built up over a week to the required daily intake, depending on age at weaning. An *ad lib* supply of water from an automatic bowl is ideal, otherwise watering two or three times daily by hand is needed during the first few weeks of lactation.

Sore knees with bare patches of skin on the front legs of the young pig indicate a shortage of milk and scrabbling for teats, or most likely a badly finished floor with a rough surface. Farrowing-crate floors should be finished with a smooth wooden trowel to prevent an over-slippery surface yet leave a not too rough finish. Washed river sand should be used in the sand/cement mix for final floor screed, as these particles are less abrasive.

Two other litter tasks remain before weaning—an anti-anaemia iron injection and castration of male pigs. Iron deficiency is a common problem with litters reared indoors, and the sow's milk contains only a limited amount. Additional iron must be administered to the young pigs by injection or oral paste. I prefer an injection of one of the proprietary iron preparations, which is a positive treatment and can be carried out on the third day with an injection into the ham of 200mg. I suspect clinical anaemia is rather rare, but the anaemic pig is weakened and predisposes to secondary infections.

Where male pigs must still be castrated, castration should be carried out before the pigs are 10 days old, as there is a rapid recovery with the younger pig, and the job can be handled as a one-man operation. In the smaller herd castration can take place at a certain age—seven days is a good time—but in the larger unit it is probably better to select one day a week and deal with all litters on that day on a blanket-treatment basis.

During this time sows and litters will need cleaning out at least once a day. With slatted floors once will be sufficient, but with solid floors twice daily will keep the sow cleaner, and generous amounts of wood shavings will help.

To summarise, the priorities are to ensure piglet protection, with a good warm environment, especially for the first 48 hours. Provided the sow is crated, comfortable, and with creep light, then most sows will farrow quickly on their own. Individual treatment at farrowing is worthwhile if you can afford the time. Routine litter tasks should be done as soon as possible and prompt veterinary attention to udder problems will lead to rapid recovery in most cases.

Creep Feeding

This is a critical management skill that is essential for growth of the young pig. Usually the floor is the best place to begin, the golden rule being 'fresh, palatable creep feed, little and often'. Any left-over food is best taken out and given to the sow.

The creep area must be well designed to prevent poaching of creep feed by the sow and the food needs to be fresh, attractive and palatable. Stale creep will be ignored, so it is best to buy small packs frequently, but check on the date of manufacture if you can. Perhaps the habit of creep feeding is more important than the actual quantity intake, but once the creep-feed consumption builds up the litter is less reliant on the sow's milk. Earlier weaning can then take place, avoiding the depletion of the sow's body reserves which used to be a feature of eight-week weaning.

Once creep-feed intake builds up—watch the young pigs' dung, which will show they are eating solid food—then is the time to put in the creep hopper. Daily servicing is important and young litters should have access to fresh clean water, although this need not necessarily be in the creep. Price per kg of creep feed does not really matter since food conversion is very good at this stage. Once young pigs are eating, most rearing problems are solved.

Many stockmen have their own tricks to encourage young pigs to eat creep feed quickly, with brown sugar, cod-liver oil, and breakfast cereals amongst the favourite appetisers. Strictly speaking, these should not be necessary, but anything that concentrates attention on this area of management is well worth doing.

It is unlikely that much creep will be eaten before seven to ten days, but it should be introduced at about five to seven days. Even at three weeks daily food intake will be well under 0·45kg per pig per day, and at four to five weeks is not likely to be much more than 0·45 to 0·68kg per head. The major factor influencing weaning weight will be the age at weaning, but correct feeding of the sow during early lactation and successful creep feeding play a large part in reaching an optimum weight at the appropriate age.

THREE-WEEK WEANING

Exactly the same routine for creep feeding can be followed for litters to be weaned between 17 and 21 days. Creep-feed intake will be very small, perhaps only a few grams per day, but it does establish the habit, and familiarises the pig with taste and feel of creep feed.

If nipple drinkers are to be used in the flat deck, then it is useful to have them fitted in the farrowing-crate area so that the young pig plays with the drinker and should use them more readily immediately post weaning.

SOW AND LITTER MANAGEMENT DURING LACTATION

After the first week the sow's food level will have been adjusted to the correct rate (see Feeding Section—Chapter 7), depending on age of weaning. Feeding can then be reduced to once daily generally, but with gilts it may be necessary to feed twice daily to maintain food intake and body condition. Where sows are crated, individual feeding is a simple matter. For group-suckling yards large nuts can be spread in the bedded area, but better still would be the provision of a bank of individual feeders which can be shared between several yards.

A watch needs to be kept on udder and teat condition: older sows may begin to dry up earlier than expected, and lumps and scratches may appear. In severe cases the only answer is to wean the litter and cull the sow, especially if she has a history of post-farrowing problems. In my experience these only get worse as the sow ages.

Litter weight at three weeks is regarded as a good indication of correct sow-feeding levels during early lactation. I am not sure that we need to weigh all litters but an occasional spot check is useful. With earlier weaning, this landmark is now much less important and attention has switched to sow productivity in terms of pigs per sow per year, and the total food cost required to produce these pigs.

Identification of all young pigs and litter groups is desirable but not entirely essential. This very much depends on the type of herd and breed-replacement policy, and the amount of recording followed through to slaughter weight. If pigs are to be earmarked, it seems sensible to do this individually if possible, or on a group or litter basis where litters are running together at three weeks. There is a wide range of earmarkers on the market which, when used with tattooing ink, give a good earmark.

WEANING

Age at Weaning

Results from the Cambridge Pig Management Scheme have shown quite clearly that there is an inverse relationship between age at weaning and the profitability of the various farms. Choice of age at weaning has been brought sharply into focus in the last few years as a result of renewed interest in early weaning between five and seven days. The number of weaners reared by each sow in the year is the critical figure in the breeding herd, and is obviously the combination of pigs reared per litter and number of litters per year. The farrowing index is most strongly influenced by age at weaning, hence this well-defined trend towards weaning earlier than the traditional eight weeks. Many herds have settled for five-week weaning, others opting for three weeks, with a pioneering minority weaning below that age. Generally speaking, in my experience the earlier the weaning, the more critical and demanding the housing and management.

Figures show that with earlier weaning there tends to be a slightly longer gap in the days between weaning and first service. Taking into account weaning age, cycle length in days (gestation, lactation and the gap between service and weaning), the following table can be constructed:

Age at weaning		No. of litters per year	Weaners per sow/ litter	Weaners per sow/ year	75% potential
7		2·7	9·7	25·6	19·2
21	days	2·5	9·5	23·7	17·75
35		2·3	9·5	21·85	16·38
48		2·0	9·5	19·00	14·25

This clearly illustrates that for maximum weaner production age at weaning must be the main consideration, and the emphasis is moving away from total concern for the weaner to a situation where it is imperative to ensure that the sow is back in pig again as soon as possible. The figures also show that performance must be somewhere near the theoretical potential, otherwise there is a drastic loss of sow productivity.

Weaning Procedures

The same procedure can be followed for three-, five- or eight-week weaning, but with earlier weaning slightly different techniques are required. Traditionally, sows were taken away from their litters gradually, spending an increasing number of hours away each day until weaning took place. This is no longer possible under modern conditions and weaning usually takes place abruptly on a fixed day of the week.

The usual choice is Thursday or Friday, which means that the sow will come on heat the middle of the following week. Services and returns to service are then a mid-week job, under better control and observation than they would be at the weekend. It also means that sows can be checked on the Friday following weaning, by which time they should be served or things are beginning to go wrong, and a check can be kept on the gap between weaning and service.

There is some controversy over feeding levels immediately before weaning. I prefer to reduce daily feed-intake levels—which may be at 5·4 to 6·35kg to 2·2 to 2·7kg daily during the last week of lactation. By this time the litter will be taking up their creep feed and the sow's milk supply will be falling off. While the udder is drying up, I feel that these lower feeding levels will give fewer problems with tender, gorged, mammary glands at weaning, which may predispose to later complications. There is a slight saving in food, but after weaning food levels can be raised again to bring the sow into rising condition at service.

The other view is that feed levels can be maintained, that back pressure in the udder will stop milk flow at weaning and the drying-up process is speeded up—although it may be uncomfortable for the sow for 48 hours. I would not recommend starving or cutting off water at weaning as there is little evidence that it does any good, and in any case it can be impractical to carry out. Weaning techniques will vary with housing systems, general body condition of the sow, feeding levels during lactation, and breed and strain of pig, as some may be far more milky than others.

There is no doubt that the physical change of weaning the sow and cessation of suckling triggers off a complicated hormonal response that will bring the sow back on heat.

Housing after weaning will vary according to the system used during lactation. Sows should not be mixed if it can be avoided, and this is one of the advantages of group suckling. Those weaned from crates or single rearing pens should go straight back into individual stalls or pens. All newly weaned sows should be housed within sight and sound of the boar. Layouts have been described in Chapter 6 which allow this to be done; for example, in the sow-stall house the end pens nearest the boar area can be used for newly weaned sows.

It is very important to move the sow to the boar for service, as research work has shown that the sow initiates the behaviour pattern when mating is about to take place. The weight and size of the boar should be matched to the sow, and the usual ratio of boars to sows is one boar to 20 to 25 sows, which will avoid overworking of boars.

Feeding between Weaning and Service

The ovulation rate of the sow will play a large part in determining the size of litter that she produces. The number of fertile ova shed by the sow is under hormonal control and these hormonal secretions can be stimulated in some circumstances by increased feed levels. This gives a similar effect to flushing in sheep, and early flushing experiments with pigs indicated that by increasing feed levels for gilts on the day of service ovulation was increased, subsequently giving more pigs at birth. More recent work has not repeated the results of these short-term flushing experiments, so practical advice from this work would point to the advisability of flushing gilts only where litter numbers in the herd are below average. With sows there may be an advantage in flushing where sows have lost weight during the previous lactation, or where numbers born have been low.

The first-litter sow is a special case, as it is always difficult to keep her in just the right condition. In this case it is a good plan to feed her generously, 2·7 to 3·6kg, between weaning and remating. Individual feeding and housing at this stage is extremely important, as it is essential that sows and gilts during this post-weaning stage get their fair share of food.

SERVICE

Heat detection should be carried out by the stockman, and with Friday weaning the first signs of heat in the sows will be seen on Tuesday. Services should be supervised and recorded, with a double

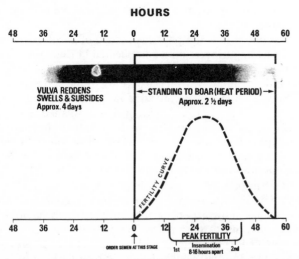

FIG. 38. *The correct time for artificial insemination and natural service.*

service for best results. First service will take place fairly soon after the sow will stand for the boar and a second service 12 to 18 hours later.

A square service pen adjacent to the boar's living quarters will speed up the job. A non-slip floor and a pen clear of any obstructions will also be of help. Where there is a large disparity in size between sow and boar a service crate can be used.

To summarise, the newly weaned sow should be in rising condition at service and should be housed adjacent to the boar. Too many thin sows are an indication of incorrect feed levels or poor distribution of feed between pregnancy and lactation, indifferent housing, and perhaps parasites. Sows should be double served on consecutive days, and a flushing effect used where numbers born are below average. The whole object of management at weaning is to reduce the gap between weaning and effective first service. This waiting time should be no more than six to seven days with five-week weaning, and a little longer with three-week weaning.

MANAGEMENT OF THE WEANER AT WEANING

Weaning at Three Weeks or Earlier

The basic technique already described for five-week weaning needs slight modification, especially of food levels. There is much practical experience with three-week weaning where daily sow-feed intake in lactation is held to a maximum of 2·7 to 3·6kg per day. When weaning at this age, sows do not get pulled down in body condition as much as they do with later weaning. The same rules apply to housing the newly weaned sow, but keener heat detection may be needed as there is usually a wider spread of time before coming on heat and a longer interval between weaning and remating with earlier-weaned sows.

With very early weaning there is not yet sufficient practical or experimental evidence to make firm recommendations. Early field reports suggest that sow-feed levels may be lifted immediately before farrowing and after weaning, and that physical contact with the boar may be necessary to assist heat detection in these very early weaned sows.

Five Weeks

At weaning, the litters will be left behind in their own familiar rearing pens, so with group suckling the litters may not even notice the departure of their dams. A change will already have been made before weaning from the creep to the growing ration, so that there are no changes of feed or housing. Extra warmth may be required to compensate for the loss of the sow's body heat, but a deep bedding of straw will put that right. Litters reared in single pens or remaining in crates are best left in their pens for a few days. In some cases pen divisions in the crate house can be lifted to allow litters to mix before removal of the sows.

This is a good time to worm pigs and also to weigh if weaning weights are required for recording purposes. Spot checks can provide a guide to the effectiveness of sow-feeding and creep-feeding techniques.

Where litters are to go into weaner houses or be mixed in weaner pools they can be moved several days after weaning—with a Friday weaning system Monday or Tuesday will be the best time for moving and mixing. Weaners should be graded and matched according to pen requirements. A spray with a pig oil/mange/insecticidal wash is a good routine as it helps to disguise litter identities and reduce fighting a little. Fighting is never very serious at this stage and weaners will quickly settle down, especially if they are well matched in size and have plenty of food and water.

Three Weeks

Early-weaned pigs need careful handling and group sizes must be sorted out for flat deck cages. To avoid extra stress in cages, litter groups may be kept entire. Fortunately the younger the pig, the less the fighting and aggression. Behaviour patterns in caged systems indicate that it may be easier to move and mix weaners inside this type of weaner house than in more traditional systems.

SOW MANAGEMENT DURING PREGNANCY

Once the sow has been served she can settle down to several months of peace and calm. Feed levels immediately after service can be brought back to the normal level of 1·8 to 2·2kg per day for a sow in good condition, well housed. Thin sows may need a higher rate for a few weeks, but overall feeding policy should be aimed at producing a fit but not over-fat sow. A steady weight gain of 13·6kg per cycle should be the target. Feed of the right quality and quantity will help to establish and maintain embryonic development to produce a strong live litter at farrowing.

A close watch must be kept for returns to service, especially at the first 20–21 day period, and if in doubt the sow should be taken to the boar. A well-identified sow and a precise record of day of service and day due to return will help the stockman with his job. Where sows are in groups a catch boar can run alongside them, and where service areas are used the sows should not be moved on until they are confirmed in pig.

Two methods of pregnancy diagnosis are now in commercial use. The vaginal biopsy method involves sampling a small piece of skin from the vulva at between 20 and 30 days after service. This is sent away for laboratory analysis, after which a rapid diagnosis of the situation can be given. A more recent development gives on-the-spot confirmation with a machine that detects particular sounds from the uterine artery of the pregnant sow after about 30 days, or picks up sounds from the foetal heartbeat or umbilical cords at a later stage. A skilled operator is needed and at present the machine is fairly expensive. Pregnancy diagnosis is going to be very important in large intensive herds, but must not be a substitute for good stockmanship. New, cheaper machines are now coming on to the market, which will make routine pregnancy testing a regular feature on many farms.

Sow comfort and contentment can be achieved under a wide range of housing conditions, providing there is a warm dry bed for her. Attention to small details such as neck tethers, occasional adjustment to girth tethers as the sow increases in size, and a close watch on feet and legs on slatted floors will make all the difference. Management routine also includes the control of internal and external parasites. Under intensive conditions the stockman accepts complete responsibility for the comfort and welfare of the pigs, and a very high standard of management is required.

Feeding once daily is acceptable but frequent checks are needed on water supply, and for sows which are totally confined it should be available at all times. Ventilation rates, house and floor temperatures, need to be kept under strict observance and review, and control equipment and thermostat settings will need to be checked and calibrated. Finally, the date of farrowing will be coming round again, and so the whole cycle recommences with another move back to the farrowing house.

MANAGEMENT OF THE WEANED PIG—POST WEANING

Tiered Cages

This is an expert job, and the management rules are still being established. Pre-heating of the room in preparation for the early weaned pig is recommended, and constant temperature, ventilation rates, and humidity levels are critical. The pigs will normally be kept in the dark except at feeding time, which takes place two or three times a day. They take readily to their pellets, but all food should be completely cleared up in each pen, so fine judgement is needed to give the right amount.

A close watch must be kept for any sign of scouring or weaners off their food, and the watering system can be used for medicinal purposes should the need arise. A regular and strict routine should be established with an extremely high standard of stockmanship and a minimum of disturbance.

Flat Decks

Pigs weaned directly into flat deck cages will need grouping by size. Environmental conditions will need checking, as will feeding spaces and water points. At three weeks there is still a very strong 'mob' instinct when feeding, so trough allowances need to be generous. Feeding and inspection routines need to be established to prevent weaners rushing around in their cages, creating chaos and confusion when disturbed unexpectedly.

Weaning into flat decks can also provide an opportunity to match up pigs by size and sex and to pen gilts and boars or hogs separately.

On some farms it has been found necessary to restrict feed for a few days immediately post weaning. This helps to prevent pigs from 'gorging' food which may trigger-off enteritis disorders and scouring. Extra trough space may be needed for a few days until *ad lib* feeding is gradually introduced. Some early weaned pigs are 'shy' drinkers and the best way to help in this case is to provide one or two cube-type drinkers in each pen. If sorting out by size is followed, then extra attention can be given to the group of pigs that are smallest in size. Pigs below 4kg are best left unweaned and can perhaps be left for a further week, or a group can be 'fostered' on to another sow for another week before weaning.

Flat deck rooms should always be managed on an 'all in—all out' basis, with special attention to cleaning and disinfection. The room must be dried out and pre-heated and a thorough check made on heating and ventilation control equipment.

Verandah Houses

This type of weaner house has internal kennels and outdoor dunging passages and requires a specialist management approach. Pig density in the kennel must be just right, otherwise pigs will dung inside. For the $2\cdot4m \times 1\cdot8m$ pen about 30 weaners at five weeks is the best number, but I have seen 50 to 60 weaners put in at three weeks of age. With smaller pigs in winter it may be necessary to cover the outside run for a few days. Panels made of sheets of corrugated polythene or perforated oil-tempered hardboard are ideal for this job.

If only a few weaners are available to put in the pen, then pen size can be reduced by packing a few bales of straw inside the kennel for a short time. These are gradually removed as the pigs grow. For three-week weaning in winter I have sometimes added supplementary heating by hanging a dull emitter heater under the kennel roof.

Weaners will have self-feeders and these should be serviced daily, giving a good opportunity to look at the pigs with the kennel lid fully lifted. Allow generous hopper space—one space to two or three weaners. As the weaners approach 18 to 20kg they will need to be split down to two groups of 15, and at 27 to 32kg they can be switched to twice-daily floor feeding to appetite. This prepares them for their final switch to fully controlled environment feeding houses.

Weaners in these houses thrive particularly well, with *ad lib* feeding, warm kennels, and slats outside in the fresh air. The odd pig will need removing from time to time and some pigs are slow to learn how to operate the nipple drinker. A building block with the hollow portion filled with concrete to within an inch of the top and placed below the nipple drinker will act as a step and catch sufficient clean water to keep the shy weaner going until it finds the secret of working the drinker. Self-fill water bowls will help to overcome this problem, but they are more likely to become fouled.

Slurry will be removed for disposal once or twice per month from the below-ground tank through the sluice gates or by vacuum tanker.

Group Suckling Yards and Weaner Pools

Groups of pigs after weaning will need daily servicing of hoppers and bedding-down with straw. Batches of pigs can be removed at 27 to 32kg and this is a good chance to pull out groups on a hog and gilt basis for separate treatment in the fattening house. If some of the larger pigs in a yard are growing ahead too quickly and look like getting over-fat, a group of 15 hogs can usually be drawn out ahead, leaving more room and food for the remainder. Group suckling will often lead to a wide range of weights, and when the yard is split up the group of smallest pigs can be *ad lib* fed for a few more days in the feeding house, which will help them to catch up a little.

It is a good time to weigh weaners when they come out of yards or verandahs. If they have been weighed at weaning this gives a good check on growth rate during this phase of their housing, and makes a starting point for measuring performance in the feeding houses. Not all weaners will be weighed, and repeated checks on a number of pens will be sufficient.

Weaner pools should always be worked on an 'all in—all out' basis and the yard completely cleaned—a job for tractor and foreloader if deep bedding has been used. This is one of the cheapest and simplest ways to house pigs during the post-weaning period, with deep bedding, generous space allowance with a covered kennel, *ad lib* feeding and water, and draught-free yards. As long as these few rules are followed management will be easy and pig performance up to target.

THE FEEDING PIG
Straw-based Systems

Trobridge Type

Pigs entering at 27–32kg will be in their final groups according to market outlet (18 to 20 for pork, 12 to 15 for bacon). Once-daily feeding by hand works very well. Calculation and adjustment of food levels can be done on a weekly basis and nuts on the floor is the best choice of feeding method.

Daily cleaning-out of the pen will be necessary and dung can be squeegeed onto a concrete apron at the front. From there it will be removed by tractor and scraper to the muck heap. The pigs can be bedded down immediately afterwards with straw or wood shavings.

Ventilation is controlled by flaps at the front and back of the pen, and careful observation of the pigs will soon indicate what adjustments are needed on a daily basis.

Pigs will have to be weighed on the outside apron and a weigher and a few portable hurdles will streamline this job. As with all feeding pigs, water bowls will need to be checked daily, a point often overlooked.

Suffolk Type

Pigs will be entering at 27–32kg in their final groups of 12 to 15. One or two slow growers can be sorted out for pork, leaving a level group for cutter or bacon production. Trough feeding twice daily by pipeline is the ideal feeding method, but a close watch is needed on feed consistency and the amount fed per pen as the pigs grow.

Alternative methods of feeding would be to use pellets in the troughs, or meal followed by water. Simple work study and the use of feed and water trucks can make this a fairly rapid job. Even with wet feeding, water should still be provided outside the kennels by a water bowl or nipple drinker. Weighing of pigs will take place in the feed passages, circulating the pigs back to their own pen, or the dung passages can be used for the job.

The Suffolk-type house is simple to manage, with good observation of pigs, a low work requirement—especially if pipeline feeding is used, and comfortable for pigs and operating staff.

Fully Enclosed, Partially Slatted House or Controlled Environment

Pigs entering this house should, for preference, come from a slatted weaner house, as they will then be familiar with floor feeding, slatted floors and nipple drinkers. They will also be settled in their pen groups of 14 or 15, but again the smaller pigs may be sorted out for pork.

The choice of feeding method is usually floor feeding from overhead dispensers which are automatically tripped two or three times a day. At these times the stockman will be able to see all the pigs feeding and watch out for first signs of anything going amiss. Feeders will need checking and calibrating from time to time as the pigs grow and pig numbers change. Some houses are fitted with adjustable pen fronts which can be gradually moved out as the pigs grow and settle into the pen.

Ventilation and temperature need watching, as any shortcomings in the environment can trigger off bouts of vice or cannibalism. Most of the control equipment is operated automatically, but thermostat settings need to be checked frequently.

Slurry will need to be removed periodically from the building and the level in the slurry channel should not be allowed to come to within about 305mm of the slats because of the danger from toxic gases and odour.

The stockman in this type of house needs to be on top of his job, and something of a technician as well. A strict routine must be established on a daily basis, a subdued lighting pattern is normally used outside feeding times, and pigs should be introduced on a particular day of the week as quietly as possible, all to keep disturbance to a minimum. Weighing of pigs approaching slaughter weight can be done in the service passage, but a weighing room should be provided at the end of the house and this is usually the best place to weigh.

Management plays a key role in this type of house, but a well-run, totally enclosed feeding house provides good working conditions, an environment in which pigs grow and convert somewhere near their optimum, and low labour requirements.

Fully Slatted House

The same management techniques can be used with the fully slatted house, but on the whole routine procedures are easier to manage than in the partially slatted house. Floors are clearly not going to be fouled, but special attention is needed for control of ventilation equipment and sensing devices. As air is exhausted below slat level, a special watch will need to be kept on slurry levels.

BOAR MANAGEMENT

Housing for the boar has already been described in a previous section (Chapter 6), and needs to be of a very high standard. It is often said that the boar is half the herd, so time spent on boar management is time well spent.

Most boars are bought in following performance testing and will need a period of isolation and hardening off before they are ready for work. Young boars should not be worked until they are about $6\frac{1}{2}$ to $7\frac{1}{2}$ months old, and a gentle introduction to a small sow that is really standing well will give him a good start and help his confidence. He should be fed to keep him fit but not over-fat, as overweight boars tend to be lazy and clumsy. A good guide would be about 2·7kg a day, but he may need more than this when working hard.

Services should be supervised and it is a mistake to run a young boar with a group of sows who may molest or injure him. Boars can often be a cause of mange spreading through the breeding herd, so regular treatment is needed. Feet and legs will need care, and a footbath of 10 per cent copper sulphate solution will help to keep his feet in trim.

Work rate can be built up until a peak work load is reached at between 10 and 12 months, and a well-managed boar should be able to cope with an average of three sows double served per week. Boars are always individuals and need careful handling at all times. Risks should not be taken with powerful older boars, and the temperament of the boars often reflects the temperament of the staff working with them.

A variation in size of boars on a unit is an advantage, and a replacement programme should be followed so that a young boar is always available for gilts and small sows. Length of working life will vary, but, to keep pace with genetic improvement, I suggest a stay in the herd of not longer than 18 months to two years.

MANAGEMENT OF THE GILT

Many gilts are now bought in, and need careful management, but the same rules apply to home-bred stock as well. On-farm performance testing means that gilts will have been grown quickly, so a hardening-off period in yards is very useful and allows legs and joints to tighten up before they start their working life.

Individual feeding is always a good policy and every opportunity should be taken to handle young gilts to overcome any nervousness and flightiness. I am not in favour of putting gilts straight into stalls or tethers, as they do not settle happily, and heat detection and service are more difficult. Straw yards with kennels and feeders make good accommodation and they can be held there comfortably until farrowing. Age and weight at first service are important, since if gilts can be mated earlier and at lighter weights the cost of feeding the sow over her life will be reduced. Surveys in the UK show average age at first service to be between 260 and 280 days, but as puberty now occurs between 170 and 200 days it should be possible for first service to take place at second or third heat when the gilt is about 200 to 220 days old and about 90–100kg in weight.

The boar needs to be the right size and weight and services should be supervised. A small proportion of gilts will fail to come on heat, and these should be culled as soon as possible. The gilt always needs special treatment, so gilt-feeding and management need special care and skill as the animal is still growing whilst producing a litter, and many infertility problems seen recently are a direct result of gilt mismanagement. Many herds replace between one-quarter and one-third of their breeding sows every year, so a large number of young sows and gilts are always needed to keep up the size of the herd.

MANAGEMENT ROUTINE FOR THE LARGE BREEDING AND FEEDING UNIT

I have discussed at length the various management and husbandry jobs that have to be carried out at various stages in pig production. These are largely a matter of detail and technical knowledge, and providing the framework of the unit has been set up correctly—and by this I mean choice of breed, feed and environment—then these applied skills will achieve the desired result in terms of pig performance and profitability.

However, as units increase in size it becomes necessary to organise labour and management on a routine basis, and a programme can be worked out for the daily and weekly work. In the routine below I am assuming a 200-sow unit with a team of three or four men, depending on the housing system and layout of the unit. Pigs are fattened for bacon and all food is purchased as compounds. All gilts are bought in from a breeding company.

Monday

Catch up with routine work after weekend.
Recording, cleaning out, etc.
Weighing of pigs approaching slaughter weight.

Tuesday

am Pigs collected for slaughter.
pm General movement and reshuffle of pigs as fattening pens are released.
Weaners weaned previous week moved into feeding herd.
Check sows weaned at end of previous week.

Wednesday

Service of weaned sows.
Castration, earmarking, litter tasks.
Check returns to service.

Thursday

Double service of weaned sows.
Manure disposal—liquids and solids.
   Litter tasks continued.
Food delivery, creep and other non-bulk feeds.

Friday

Weaning.
Recording updated.
Preparation for weekend.

Saturday and Sunday
As much time off as possible.
Once-daily feeding of breeding stock.
Feeding stock may miss one of their afternoon feeds.

Several other jobs will have to be fitted into this pattern, including bulk-food delivery, delivery of breeding gilts and boars, veterinary consultation, staff holidays. In my opinion, visits to bacon factory, demonstrations, open days and lectures are necessary to keep in touch with what is happening in the pig world.

Many variations on this routine can be worked out. It will need amending and updating according to the size of the unit, feed preparation policy, manure disposal, and age of weaning. It does give staff a positive work programme and the whole week is focused around the key management factors of weaning and service.

With three-week weaning systems, sows should be weaned on Thursday to make sure all sows are served before the following weekend, ie, nine to 10 days later.

Chapter 9

MANAGEMENT—Staff

THE INCREASE in unit size and change in techniques in the pig industry have greatly altered the role of labour in pig production.

Training has a vital part to play, as the modern stockman needs to be proficient in practical tasks and yet he also requires a good technical background in management, feeding, housing and economics. Facilities for training are now available at a large number of County Agricultural Colleges and day-release courses, and agricultural education has improved rapidly over the last few years. The ATB has played a large part in this, with training of management at all levels, and they have issued a first-class training handbook on pig production. Some commercial companies have introduced their own training schemes, and as large breeding and marketing organisations become more interested in pig farming this seems a likely pattern.

A particular feature of recent courses has been the specialisation that has taken place at several colleges including Usk, Humberside, and Norfolk. These courses vary in length, but I like the sandwich course approach followed by Usk with which I was involved while at NAC. Students on this residential course, which lasts for two years, must already have completed some basic agricultural education. The first six months are spent in college on theoretical and laboratory work, followed by two six-month periods on two different, carefully selected modern pig farms. This sandwich part of the training is valuable for the practical experience gained, measured against their college lectures. Project work is undertaken which can be valuable for the participating farmers. In my experience these students arriving on the farm each March and September gave a fillip to regular members of the pig team. The last term of the course is spent in a bacon factory or abattoir to gain some insight into the processing side of the business. The course is naturally rounded off with a series of examinations, and each year the dozen or so students have had no difficulty in finding key posts on farms throughout the country. This is an ideal course for the young man intending to make a career of stockmanship.

The other courses are shorter. Twelve weeks at Humberside, 20 weeks at Norfolk. These shorter courses are probably better for people who already have practical experience, and could even be feasible on extended 'leave' for working stockmen.

I believe these men turned out from our specialist colleges have a major contribution to make to the pig industry and will provide the backbone of our technical staff over the coming years.

Some on-farm training remains to be done, and with our larger units this is both possible and practical, as this situation provides opportunity for promotion to managerial jobs. Every farmer or manager has his own ideas about how things should be done, and if staff are trained in his methods a better relationship is likely to result. Part of this training lies in visits to demonstrations, other farms, bacon factories, etc.

In some cases men with no previous experience of pigs have been willing to move into the country to take up jobs on pig units. Where on-farm training can be given, and with a completely open-minded approach, these tactics have on occasions been very successful.

On-farm training has been given a tremendous boost by the development and activities of the Agricultural Training Board. A large number of courses are run by expert staff throughout the country, and each county has specialist staff able to give specific advice and recommendations on training.

The ATB now offers some excellent 'off-farm' courses which allow trained managers and stockmen to pass on their skills to their colleagues and staff. Tailor-made short courses are available for craft, supervisory and specialist farm staff to develop their ability to instruct and achieve results through a proper appreciation of man-management skills.

Courses at the Training Centre at the NAC of particular interest include 'Man Management, human relations and communications', 'Effective Supervision', 'Instructional Techniques', and 'Work Organisation'.

The work of the ATB has been underrated and I believe this organisation has an important role to play in both on-farm and off-farm training of the staff employed in pig production.

One other thought on education and training. I regret that there is no national award for training in pig husbandry. A national qualification could add to the status and improve the image of these key men on our pig farms.

The new-style stockman now has a much greater responsibility in terms of pig numbers and effectively controls the larger part of the capital invested in the enterprise, while total cost of labour, at about 8 to 10 per cent, is still relatively low.

Good, skilled staff are now becoming a limiting factor in the growth of the pig industry and since, by the nature of the industry, chances of promotion are limited, some means must be found to maintain the interest and incentive of well-trained men.

Increased mechanisation and slatted floors will help to remove much of the drudgery associated with the traditional pigman's job, but there is a limit to which automation can be carried, and plans in this direction should be designed to leave staff with more time to inspect and observe their stock. The real answer, I believe, lies in a combination of improved status and financial reward. If each member of staff has his own area of responsibility and a bonus scheme linked to the results of his own effort, these objectives are partly met. Wage structures have been worked out, with additional rates for craftsmen into which category most skilled stockmen will fall, but a real effort must be made to work out a bonus scheme on top of this to lift the basic rate.

On our larger units a system can usually be found which gives a neat subdivision of responsibility between various sections of the farm operation. A simple job specification can then be arrived at for each section, and targets agreed which can be reviewed periodically, perhaps six-monthly. A bonus scheme can then be devised which is linked to recording and which is directly related to the results in each particular section. The bonus must be a realistic amount, paid regularly, perhaps each month, and must be based on factors over which the individual member of staff has direct control. It should no longer be necessary for farm staff to work long hours of overtime to make a living.

These methods also make management control easier, as staff have clearly defined responsibilities and an incentive to fulfil them thoroughly and carefully.

Apart from immediate financial reward, there is the question of housing.

Housing for farm staff has been a contentious area for many years. Some rural housing has been improved over recent years to compete with the best in urban development, and it can no longer be said that in some cases 'the pigs are housed better than the staff'. Problems also occur with isolation as many rural bus services have been withdrawn and those that remain are few and far between. Car-owning—and driving—is now an essential part of country living. A large part of keeping staff settled lies in keeping wives and families happy, and housing and transport play a most vital part in this.

The provision of housing for farm staff has been transformed by the Rent (Agriculture) Act 1976. This major change in the law in effect sweeps away the old 'tied-cottage' legislation in which a farm worker lost possession of his house when he left a particular job in which the house was owned and provided by his employer.

In general terms, the Act provides that a person who has worked whole time in agriculture for at least two years, or who becomes incapable of work in agriculture in consequence of a qualifying injury or disease, and who occupies a house which is provided by his employer, is a protected occupier. When his employment in agriculture ends, he becomes a statutory tenant. Protected occupiers and statutory tenants can be evicted if a court decides that there has been a tenancy offence. Otherwise the employer or ex-employer providing the house can regain possession only if suitable alternative accommodation is made available for the existing occupier.

The Rent (Agriculture) Act thus affords protection to agricultural workers who are not protected under the Rent Act 1968 because they pay little or no rent. It also amends the 1968 Act so that agricultural workers who have Rent Act tenancies are given the same protection as they would have had under the new Act.

It may be that the employer himself can provide or can arrange suitable alternative accommodation. If he cannot reasonably do so, the alternative accommodation may be provided by the local Housing Authority, who are obliged to use their best endeavours to provide this when needed on agricultural grounds. Disputes about the suitability of the alternative accommodation can be decided by the courts in the last resort, but the basic criteria are laid down in the Act.

If a local authority is to be asked to provide the re-housing, the employer must show that it is in the interests of efficient agriculture that the re-housing should take place, to make way for an incoming worker. This question of efficient agriculture may be examined by a local 'Agricultural Dwelling House Advisory Committee' (ADHAC). This is only a brief summary of the major provisions of this new piece of legislation and is taken from an excellent publication called 'A Guide to the Rent (Agriculture) Act 1976' by Moira Constable, working from the Arthur Rank Centre at the NAC.

The Act is very complex, and in difficult or complicated cases legal advice should be sought. The Act came into force in January 1977 and it is probably too early to judge how legislation is working. There was a good deal of criticism by various parties as the legislation was being drafted, especially of the difficult role of the Agricultural Dwelling House Advisory Committee (ADHAC). However, the Department of Environment, who are effectively responsible for the operation of the legislation, report that in the first six months (January–June 1977), 'Nearly 300 farm workers or ex-workers have been rehoused without going through the courts during this period, farmers have been able to regain possession of their cottages when they can show agricultural need, and local authorities have generally been able to meet the demand for rehousing quickly from within existing resources.'

Problem areas remain, including the provision of housing for the retired worker and, of course, there will be hardship in certain individual cases.

Overall, the new Act appears to be working, but it does not solve the problem of the man who likes to own his own home, which is the ambition of many key farm workers. This whole area of home owning is explored in detail by the Reverend Canon Peter Buckler of the Arthur Rank Centre at the NAC in a leaflet entitled 'For Everyman his own Castle—Opportunities for Home Ownership' for agricultural workers. Various factors about mortgages are discussed and several methods by which the employer might help in the purchase of property —and all this against the background of the agricultural employee.

Working conditions have been generally much improved, but there is still some way to go. There is now much less of the brush-and-shovel work, and well-planned units and work study can remove much of the dirty work. Provision of a changing room, where protective clothing and footwear can be left behind along with much of the inevitable smell, is a great advantage, and 'suitable and sufficient washing facilities' and 'suitable and sufficient sanitary conveniences', kept clean and provided with clean water, soap, and clean towels, are required by law (Agriculture [Safety, Health and Welfare Provisions] Act 1974). Such things as closed-circuit television between farrowing house and stockman's house may seem something of a luxury, but they will come slowly.

Beiefly then, the modern pig unit needs well-trained reliable staff who are willing and able to accept responsibility. In addition, consultation and communication between management and staff is essential so that all staff have an overall picture of what is happening on the unit, and any difficulties can be cleared up quickly.

These men will expect and deserve living and working conditions and financial rewards comparable to those for skilled workers in any other industry. Many of them will look elsewhere if such conditions are not provided, and that would be a great loss to the pig industry, which it can ill-afford.

Finally, I quote an example of a job specification for a manager in charge of a 250-sow unit. This job description is very simple and the information can be updated and changed as required to suit the particular farm and situation.

Job Description

JOB TITLE	Farm Manager.
PLACE OF WORK	White House Farm, Great Ashton, Blankshire.

RESPONSIBLE TO	Mr Tom Howarth, Farmer/Owner.
CONDITIONS	Generally out of doors and around buildings, but some office work involved.
GENERAL DESCRIPTION OF JOB	Manager in charge of 250 sows and progeny fattened for cutter and bacon production. Responsible directly to owner for day-to-day control and management of all aspects of the enterprise. Other farm staff will report directly to you.
RESPONSIBILITIES AND KEY TASKS	1. Fecundity, feeding and management of all sows and fattening pigs. 2. Overall recording of breeding and feeding-herd performances. 3. Supervision and training of other staff employed. 4. Ordering of feed and veterinary supplies. 5. Selection of stock for breeding and for slaughter.

Chapter 10

HEALTH

It is not the intention of this book to string together a long list of pig diseases, their diagnosis and treatment. This has already been done by many competent and authoritative publications, and a large amount of investigation and research work, which is well reported, is increasing our knowledge of pig diseases and their prevention. I intend therefore to concentrate entirely on preventive medicine.

Good health is a vital component of profitable pig production, but the growth and development of large-scale intensive pig units is making disease control and eradication increasingly difficult. Well-planned housing, correct nutrition, and good management are essential as a background for disease prevention, but the source and type of breeding stock used are also important.

Losses from disease in the national pig herd run to many millions of pounds per year. The actual cost is difficult to arrive at but several estimates have been made, some in the region of several million pounds.

In some instances this may be in a spectacular form such as an outbreak of TGE or SVD, but more usually losses occur in a chronic form such as infertility in breeding stock, pre-weaning mortality, post-weaning scours or respiratory disease in the fattening herd. It is these chronic troubles that eat away at the profits in pig production, and a great deal of attention is now being directed towards a policy of disease prevention for farm livestock which will limit these losses.

One such estimate of losses is based on the Government's inquiry into the veterinary profession known as the Swann Report and published in 1975.

Figures used in the report were for the three years from 1968 to 1971. The UK national herd varied from 885,000 to 953,000 in those years, and an output of 10·3 pigs born per litter and 19·88 pigs born alive per year were used.

The following tables show that the main losses were pre-weaning, with smaller losses post-weaning. The total cost of these losses was in the region of £20 million over a three-year period, taking into account

Pig gross output for the UK over three June–May years

	1968–69	1969–70	1970–71
Average number of sows and gilts (thousands)	885	918	953
Number of pigs born alive a sow	19·88	19·88	19·88
Total number of pigs born alive (thousands)	17,594	18,250	18,946

Estimated average annual losses of young pigs in the UK between 1968–71 at 1970–71 values

	Number of animals (thousands)	Resources lost	
		Value in £ per head	Total £'000
Pre weaning	3,012	4	12,048
Post weaning	513	15	7,965
Total	3,525		20,013

Livestock losses were adjusted downwards to 2,996, 505 and 3,471 to allow for unofficial trade, reducing total resources lost to £19,439,000.

costs of production and allowances for capital investment and management.

At today's prices, even with a reduced national herd, the losses must be running at £10 million per year. Saving a proportion of these pigs must surely cost only a fraction of this sum and effort must be directed at more research, better veterinary services, improved utilisation of these services and a better understanding of the interaction between health, housing, feeding and management at farm level.

Another approach was adopted by Mike Muirhead, a Yorkshire veterinary surgeon who specialises in pig work. The chart on page 187 is based on a 100-sow herd producing 2,000 bacon pigs per year. The costs were calculated from recorded disease levels in intensive pig units, using a 'target' system for arriving at disease levels. The main losses are shown to be a result of poor sow reproductivity in the breeding herd and atrophic rhinitis in the feeding herd (see chart on sow losses on page 187).

In this chapter I would like to examine the general background to disease prevention and the practical steps that can be taken at farm level, and then to look briefly at the interaction between disease and pig management under intensive conditions.

HEALTH SCHEMES
The Government Health Scheme

This scheme was launched in 1968 following the eradication of swine fever in the mid-1960s. It is designed to control and reduce the incidence of pig disease, allowing full advantage to be taken of genetic improvement, and thus increasing the profitability of the industry and increasing the potential for export of livestock. Membership is limited to MLC's Pig Improvement Scheme herds and to a small number of other special herds including breeding companies who are submitting stock for

Pig losses in 100 sow herd

Condition	Treatment £	Loss or mortality	Performance loss	Disease level*	Cost net 1 year £	Recurring cost £
Foot-and-mouth	—	100%	100%	—	20,000	Nil
Swine vesicular disease	—	100%	100%	—	20,000	Nil
Swine fever	—	100%	100%	—	20,000	Nil
Farrowing rate 70%	—	320 pigs	—	—	5,440	5,440
Rhinitis	1,322	40 pigs	3,250	H	5,172	variable 50%
Aujesky's disease	150	400 pigs	variable	H	4,950	Insignificant, variable
Transmissible gastro-enteritis	—	230 pigs	—	H	3,910	Nil
Enzootic pneumonia	105	20 pigs	0·2 FCR loss	M	2,605	2,605
Infertility viruses	—	176 pigs	—	M	2,992	2,992
Repeat services	—	86 pigs	—	A	1,462	1,462
Abortion	—	38 pigs	—	M	646	646
Not in pig	—	44 pigs	—	A	748	748
Dysentery	675	10 pigs	—	L	845	845
Stillbirths	—	46 pigs	—	A	782	782
Laid on	—	46 pigs	—	A	782	782
Low viability	—	96 pigs	—	A	1,632	1,632
Post weaning	variable	35 pigs	variable	A	700	700
Fattening loss	—	30 pigs	—	A	900	900
Lactation losses	35	48 pigs	—	L	851	851

* Disease level—L=low, M=moderate, H=high, A=average.

central performance testing. The advantages of basing the health scheme on these MLC herds are that:

(a) Some protection is given to progeny-testing stations and this reduces the possibility of introduction of disease.
(b) The herds in the MLC scheme have a high standard of management, which is essential for investigational work.
(c) The Nucleus and Reserve herds provide a source of genetically improved breeding stock, and improved health is passed on to the pig industry along with the improved genetic material.
(d) Genetic progress can be more easily identified in the absence of disease.

The scheme is operated under close veterinary supervision of member herds with investigation of all illness by clinical post-mortem and laboratory methods, and recommendation of appropriate action to be taken by the owner. The success of the scheme depends on close co-operation between breeders, veterinary surgeons, MLC field staff, and MAFF departments. The scheme provides for quarterly inspection of the herd made alternately by the farmer's own vet at the Ministry's expense, and by a Ministry Veterinary Officer. It is seen as a flexible arrangement which can be improved and which will lead to a great deal of information being obtained on disease problems and their cost, at the same time highlighting preventive measures which will benefit the whole industry.

Other Health Schemes

Health schemes have been run by a number of organisations involved in the pig industry, including food compounders and breeding companies. Their integrated marketing schemes often involve nucleus, multiplication and commercial meat-producing farms, and supervision is carried out by a company veterinarian in co-operation with the owner's own veterinary surgeon. Strict discipline can be maintained, especially by breeding companies who have modelled their schemes on the pattern of the Government Health Scheme.

Pig Health Control Association

This scheme was set up in 1959 by a number of pedigree breeders to establish a register of herds free from enzootic pneumonia. By the beginning of 1976 about 200 herds had participated for varying lengths of time and over 90 had been officially registered as free from the disease. These herds are placed on List 'A' of the PHC association. Breakdowns do occur and the list is revised from time to time.

Minimal Disease

In the early 1960s, following work in the USA and Canada, the principle of minimal-disease herds was introduced into the UK. In the States the herds were designated SPF (Special Pathogen Free), but in this country they are known as Minimal Disease (MD). Herds are established by hysterectomy, and commercial laboratories were set up for this purpose.

The economical advantages claimed for MD herds included lower mortality, greater feed efficiency, and better growth as a result of relative freedom from disease. A number of MD herds have been established in this country by individual farmers and breeding organisations, but there have been a few breakdowns. Once a primary MD herd has been set up it is then relatively cheap and easy to set up a series of linked secondary MD herds.

Whilst there is no problem in establishing the original or primary herd, there is considerable difficulty in maintaining their disease-free status on the farm. MD pigs are usually free of disease such as skin parasites, worms, enzootic pneumonia and swine dysentery. Commercial experience has given encouraging results, and MD pigs have performed well under all systems of pig production.

ESTABLISHING A NEW HERD
Source of Stock

Farmers setting up a new unit will obviously need to be extremely careful in their selection of initial stock. Some guidance is provided by membership of the Government Pig Health Scheme. List 'A' of the PHCA or MD herds. Ideally, all boars and gilts would be obtained from one farm or multiplication unit, the gilts will of course be maiden gilts about 86 to 91kg liveweight. Buying pigs from a variety of sources should be avoided. Most of these herds will be, by definition, under some form of veterinary supervision, so that checks can be made about the health status of the herd. Stock purchased from these sources should be free from respiratory diseases and external parasites, and with the adoption of reasonable precautions freedom from disease should be maintained.

Farm Precautions
Isolation

Ideally, new units should be established as far as possible from other stock, especially other pigs. This helps to avoid infection by transport, staff, and potential airborne disease.

Security

The most obvious source of infection to a pig unit, apart from other pigs, is in general terms the visitor—human, animal, wildlife, and transport. To restrict access a 2·4m-high chain-link fence is recommended, with one entrance only which should be well signposted with clear directions. This entrance should normally be locked, with a bell to summon attention.

A vehicle-wheel dip should be placed inside the entrance. This wheel dip should be at least 3·6m long and 0·3m deep, and is filled with a Ministry-approved disinfectant. An office or gatehouse near the entrance will be used by the stockmen for changing and storing their clothes. Protective clothing—caps, boots, overalls—should be worn during working hours. These security arrangements will allow visitors to be controlled and to be provided with protective clothing and shoes when they are admitted. On MD units especially it is good sound practice to provide shower facilities and to ensure that staff take showers in and out of the premises on a daily basis.

Transport

Transport collecting stock for slaughter should not be allowed inside the unit. A loading bay should be planned on the perimeter of the unit, to which pigs are moved when ready for despatch. Transport delivering breeding stock should only be permitted to approach the isolation area which should be attached to the main farm, and drivers should not be allowed to come into the premises. Bulk food can be delivered by vehicles which are kept outside the main perimeter fence, and food is blown into strategically sited bulk-storage bins.

Other Precautions

All buildings should be planned to exclude birds which may carry disease, and routine control of vermin is essential for the same reason. Vehicles and equipment should not be borrowed from neighbouring farmers. I am thinking particularly of slurry equipment and pig weighers. Farm staff should not be allowed to keep pigs at home as this can put the entire unit at risk, especially where a few weaners might be bought in for fattening. Arrangements should be made for carcase disposal by incineration or by burying at the appropriate depth in accordance with Ministry regulations.

ISOLATION AND INTEGRATION OF STOCK

Isolation of newly purchased stock will not completely protect the unit, but it is a practical precaution where gilts and boars are bought in. A building outside the main area with its own disinfection control, food supply, tools and equipment is ideal. A set of yards with feeders gives good facilities for observation and inspection. Gilts and boars should remain in isolation for at least 20 days before moving to the main unit. Some veterinarians now recommend an 'early challenge' to incoming stock by moving a batch of fattening pigs out to join them about 14 to 20 days after arrival, then allowing a further 14 days before bringing them into the unit if they are still free of disease.

On introduction to the main unit the maiden gilts will be housed as near as possible to adult breeding stock, ideally in a service area or pens in the sow accommodation. This will allow some immunity to be built up in the newly introduced stock before they are served.

These are the ideal requirements, and even a new unit carefully planned at the drawing board is unlikely to meet all of them. However difficult, the existing farm should try to carry out some of these precautions such as vehicle dips, disinfectant sprays for vehicles, loading ramps, limitation of visitors, and isolation of incoming stock.

Fortunately, veterinary surgeons are increasingly aware of the problems involved in large-scale intensive pig production, and specialisation is taking place within their profession. The veterinary specialist should be called in at the planning stage when advice can be given on details of housing and environment, on pig movement and feeding practices, as well as the particular problems to be met in setting up a new pig unit. Once the unit is established, then routine preventive medicine procedures can be agreed upon.

Arrangements will need working out for each fa
with the help of veterinary advice, will go a long w
disease control at least possible cost.

HERD HEALTH PROGRAM

Now that the general framework of a preventive m..
been drawn up, it is possible to set out a detailed health programmu .
the pig unit. These programmes are already being prepared by veterinary
specialists for use in new intensive units, but they can also be used with
only slight modification for existing pig units. In most cases the plan
would be agreed with the owner or manager of the unit and would be
based on quarterly visits by the veterinary surgeon (or more frequently
in some units), backed up by 'phone advice as required. There would
also be some on-farm training for the manager or stockmen in some
aspects of routine treatment.

Health Programme for Established or New Units

Stock
(1) Maiden gilts bought from proven source, and they should be
isolated on arrival.
Service to take place no sooner than second heat.
(2) All incoming stock should be wormed with broad-spectrum anthel-
mintics on arrival.
(3) All stock should have been vaccinated against swine erysipelas
before arrival. Booster doses to be given at six-monthly intervals
to adult breeding stock thereafter.

Housing
(1) All work should be completed and concrete fully dried out before
stock arrives.
(2) With new stock on new concrete, provision should be made for a
footbath to be used twice weekly.

Staff
(1) Emphasis placed on disease control and the reasons behind it.
Enthusiasm must be generated about presentation of the unit,
productivity and profitability.
(2) Staff duties should be detailed on a daily work programme basis,
with weekend rotas agreed.

Recording
Recording and monitoring systems to be agreed and started as the
unit is set up.

Routines of Preventive Medicine for Health Maintenance

Much of this has already been covered in the Management section
(Chapter 8), but this summary highlights the connection between
management and good health.

glets

(a) Birth—clip teeth.
(b) Spray navels at birth with suitable preparation or aerosol.
(c) Three days—iron injection, which should contain 200mg iron complex.
(d) Castration—any time up to four weeks of age—suggest at four to seven days.
(e) Worm dosing—in some herds this is unnecessary, but to ensure satisfactory status either:
  (i) take a sample of faeces of weaners every three months, or
  (ii) worm at six to eight weeks of age.

Sows

(a) Worming—one week before farrowing with a broad-spectrum wormer.
(b) Mange dressing—one week before farrowing with a suitable dressing.
(c) Booster erysipelas vaccination—after initial two doses before gilts arrive at each weaning time 2cc vaccine.
(d) Weight gain—weight at each weaning time. For ideal performance a weight gain of about 13·6kg at each of the first four weaning times is required.

Boars

(a) 3cc erysipelas vaccine every six months after initial course.
(b) Broad-spectrum worm dose every six months.
(c) Mange dress every six months or more frequently as required.
(d) Service—double service of sows at about 12–24 hour intervals is essential.

Recording

(a) Monitor performance.
(b) Monitor profitability.
(c) Set forward targets and budgets, which will need constant review and updating.

Hygiene

(a) Cleanliness of housing, surroundings and pigs. Cleanliness also has a beneficial psychological effect on staff. A high standard will help to improve the working environment and reduce disease incidence.
(b) A programme of cleaning and disinfection should be worked out appropriate to the farm and management system.
(c) Depopulation on a periodic basis with fumigation or disinfection of sections of the unit.

Health Problems Associated with Intensive Systems

In spite of all these well-planned programmes and precautions, problems do arise. They should not be major disasters such as TGE as most of the agents should have been excluded, and the monitoring programme should pick up signs of chronic infertility at an early stage. They are more likely to be niggling and chronic problems, some of which will be outside normal experience as we are often working on the fringe of knowledge in intensive livestock production.

Sows

Breeding stock in stalls seem prone to lameness and foot troubles. Hardening off of gilts on arrival, careful selection on legs and conformation, will help to reduce this problem, as well as the footbath treatment mentioned earlier. I found that a major cause of lameness could be traced to faulty slatted floors. Some concrete slats are delivered with very rough edges, and these should be ground off at the corners with a carborundum stone. Watch the slat width; in my experience it should be no more than 12·7mm and run parallel with the sow.

Sows in partially slatted stalls without bedding can be kept much cleaner if they are given a handful of sawdust daily on their beds. This gives just a bit of extra comfort and prevents some of the dung clinging to them. Sows in tethers seem more prone to prolapse than sows housed in other systems and the length of the lying area and slope of the bed should be checked, as the back end of the sow needs support when she is heavy in pig. Tether design is now much improved, but a watch should be kept for chafing and rubbing—a spot of pig oil or liquid paraffin will help to prevent this.

In very cold weather space heating can be used in a sow-stall house to boost the temperature, and in tether houses a generous bedding of straw will keep the sows warmer.

Infertility still remains one of the major non-infectious diseases of the breeding herd, and can be largely attributed to faulty management and feeding. For further background, reference should be made to the appropriate sections in Chapter 8 on Stock Management.

Stress

Stress is another major problem in pigs of all ages and sizes but this is an area where present knowledge is limited. A reduction in the number of times the sow is moved must help. As the adult breeding sow appears to be very aggressive on being mixed with other sows this should be avoided wherever possible. Group size and stocking density are two other areas where stress is involved, and welfare recommendations have provided a good guide on these points.

G

Vices

No book would be complete without a mention of tail biting and cannibalism, but again we are in an area about which very little is known. The environment of the pigs appears to have a direct effect on outbreaks of tail biting. Some factors which seem to trigger it off are:

A dry, dusty atmosphere associated with meal feeding.

Too high a temperature, which is probably a result of faulty ventilation.

Wide fluctuations in environmental conditions, with poor distribution and direction of incoming air.

Overstocking of pens and incorrect stocking density.

A variety of unknowns, including too much fibre in the diet, insufficient light or too much light, lack of bedding and boredom, too much disturbance and irregular feeding.

Certainly tail biting is always a bigger problem in the intensive house, and is rarely seen in bedded systems. In large feeding houses I believe ventilation to be a main factor, especially where there is poor air distribution.

Where houses are fitted with open penning which the pigs can see through and smell their adjacent pen mates, there appears to be a much better behaviour pattern and less outbreaks of tail biting. Finally, to take a defeatist line on this point, I recommend the hygienic docking of tails at birth. I again emphasise that only the tip needs to be removed. After this treatment I have very rarely seen a case of tail biting over a period of years. It is interesting to note that bacon factories and abbattoirs have recorded fewer cases of carcase condemnation where tail docking has been carried out.

SPECIALISATION

One encouraging feature of health control and disease prevention is the established growth and development of the Pig Veterinary Society. This is an association of veterinary surgeons from within private practices, Ministry departments and commercial organisations who have a specific interest in all aspects of pig production. Regular meetings are held and proceedings are now published on a regular basis. It is essential all facets of the industry work together, and the following chart prepared by Mike Muirhead gives a good indication of a team approach to health and production problems.

This chart sets our standards for a typical pig unit which should be agreed by the veterinary adviser and manager. Action can then be taken at the 'interference' levels indicated. This may initially be short-term treatment by the vet, but will lead to a deep investigation and discussion about the whole range of potential causal factors whether they be environmental, nutritional or managemental in origin.

4–5 week Weaning	Target	Interference Level	MLC Top 33% Herds
Services	100	100	
Weaning to service interval days	7	9	
Returns %	6	12	
Abortions %	0·8	2·5	
Infertile %	2	5	
*Farrowing rate %	89	80	
Sow deaths p.a. %	2·2	3	
Farrowing %	89	80	
No. alive/litter	10·9	10	10·8
% stillbirths	5	8	
% Mummified	0·5	1	
No. weaned/litter	9·6	9·0	9·4
% deaths to weaning	8·12	12·18	13
Litter scatter %	10	18	
Laid on %	5	7	
Congenital defects %	0·5	1·5	
Low viability %	1·5	3	
Starvation %	1	3	
Deaths scour %	0·5	2	
Miscellaneous deaths %	3	5	
Scour litters %	4	10	
Litters sow/year	2·25	2·0	2·0
Pigs/sow/year	21	19	18·8
Post weaning deaths	2	3	
Fattening deaths	1·5	2·5	1·4
Sow culls/100 sows/month	3 or 36% p.a.		

* Farrowing rate $= \dfrac{\text{No. farrowing}}{\text{No. services}} \times 100$

Chapter 11

RECORDING AND MANAGEMENT CONTROL

THE IMPORTANCE of recording the overall performance of the herd cannot be over-emphasised, as a continuous and accurate check on pig performance is essential. An analysis of this performance will pinpoint any weaknesses that exist and give information which can be used to calculate the profitability of the herd, and so show where better management is needed. Recording is only a means to an end, and any recording system should be simple and precise and be directed towards improving pig performance and profit. In many herds a whole collection of figures are made which are never utilised or are in themselves of no value. The main criteria are total food used and total pig meat sold; the cost of the food and the cash value of the pig meat sold.

An overall scheme should be drawn up which is feasible for staff to operate, which can be processed and interpreted without delay, and which is relevant to the production system. Obviously a breeding multiplication unit will require a quite different set of records than those of a large commercial unit. Recording data collected for the physical performance of stock will also give valuable veterinary information and the one set of records will be adequate for both purposes. It may be useful from the veterinary point of view to amplify causes of death and to record veterinary treatment, thus building up a picture of physical performance against the health background of the herd. Pig recording can also act as a sound basis for calculating bonus systems, giving an added incentive to staff involved in record collection.

Records have also been used in the past by breeders selling stock to authenticate claims for the performance of their herd. This particular use of recording is now much less important, having been superseded by information supplied by MLC and other organisations from progeny and performance testing. Herd records on a comparative basis can be misleading because of differing husbandry, management, and feeding practices, and should be interpreted carefully.

RECORDING SCHEMES

It would be useful to have a brief look at recording schemes in use at present. The NPBA have been active in this field for many years, but this was mainly litter recording on a pedigree family basis for use in the show-ring. However, they were responsible for initiating the first pig recording scheme in the early 1950s. This was taken over by PIDA who did much pioneering work on national pig recording, and this work eventually formed the basis for the present MLC scheme.

MLC NATIONAL FEED RECORDING SCHEME

This scheme concentrates on pig-feed consumption in relation to numbers, weights and grading, and the total cost involved. It helps producers to record these facts with a set of pro-forma which are filled in on the farm on a monthly basis and then sent to the regional MLC office for processing by computer. Detailed results are produced on a six-monthly basis with comparative standards for guidance. Once the scheme is under way a set of rolling six-monthly figures are provided each month. MLC field-development officers are able to help with interpretation of records and give on-the-spot advice for putting things right where necessary. A supplementary and optional part of this scheme can provide a six-monthly trading account, which pinpoints profit, feed and labour costs per £100 gross output.

UNIVERSITY RECORDING SCHEMES

Perhaps the best known of these is the Cambridge University Pig Management Scheme, which takes in a sample of farms in East Anglia —about 90 in all—and records and analyses their physical and financial performances on an annual basis. This scheme has built up a valuable long-term record of pig performance on these selected farms over a number of years. The results are widely quoted and are classified on a graded basis so that useful comparisons can be made.

The University of Exeter Agricultural Economics Unit records and publishes the results from approximately 70 farms in Cornwall, Devon and Dorset, and has built up a useful series of comparative information over the years.

OTHER RECORDING SCHEMES

Many other organisations run recording schemes, including ADAS whose information is set out in Short Term Leaflet No. 121 called 'Sow-breeding Calendars and Records'.

The overall business and financial approach is covered in a joint ADAS/NFU Farm Business Record Book which provides separate sections for the various farm enterprises.

Many feed compounders, especially where integration is taking place, offer a feed-recording service which is backed up by advisory visits and the provision of visual aids such as record cards, feed charts, etc. A similar service is run by breeding companies who will obviously require detailed information on the performance of their pigs, and breed societies still carry on with litter registration and recording.

Finally, under this umbrella, the various farm management consultancy services provide feed-recording schemes.

Finding the right level of recording can be difficult, and it is easy to be critical of recording schemes. Perhaps the most disappointing feature is that only relatively few farmers record under these schemes, or indeed at all. I suspect that many farmers record under several schemes with one set of records—this is fairly easy—and this further reduces the total number of pig farmers recording. Those who do record tend to be the more progressive and younger business-minded farmers, but I think attitudes are changing, which is encouraging.

One major shortcoming of most of these schemes is that they tend to be retrospective and fail to provide up-to-date information, to enable realistic management-control decisions to be taken on the spot. Some records kept are limited to physical performance only without the necessary emphasis on the translation of this factor into financial terms, and this can be very misleading. The University figures do provide the pig industry with comparative performance figures and it is encouraging to see that the Cambridge reports now include extra information. This additional section includes forecasts and projections in the inevitable event of higher costs of food and labour, and the effect on profits.

The MLC Scheme is now throwing up some interesting information on comparisons on the farm between various management systems such as wet and dry feeding. This will be extremely valuable for the industry, as there is plenty of experimental and research work on these points but very little confirmation at commercial level.

With the growth of larger units and the increasingly business-like approach to pig production there have been some interesting developments in the field of computer recording.

Linked to this has been a move towards specialised consultancy work and a number of firms are active in this field. MLC also operate a business consultancy service including 'Pig Plan'. This is a management service, and subscribers to this monitoring system are given regularly updated cash flows and production forecasts.

PRACTICAL RECORDING IN COMMERCIAL UNIT

Basically two distinct types of information are required:

Day-to-day management.

Long-term planning.

This two-tier system gives some on-the-spot control from information gathered from day-to-day operation which can be of help in long-term planning, budgetary and financial control, as well as giving a composite overall picture.

Day-to-Day Management

Any recording scheme or method is only as good as the information collected by the stockman on a daily basis. To do the job effectively and simply he needs a strong pocket notebook for services, returns and farrowings. This can be supplemented by a set of litter record cards which are completed daily and can be read at a glance. These should be located near the sow and litter, and at weaning this information should be transferred to a cumulative record card for each sow.

Food usage can be recorded on a Barn Sheet which gives a generous space for each day of the month, and which can also carry a record of suckler deaths as well as farrowings and numbers of pigs weaned.

A central service register is extremely useful as it may give a first indication of problems such as infertility with a particular boar.

Where sows are in stalls a board or card must be provided for each sow with the following information:

Date of service ....

Date due to return ....

Date due to farrow ....

The Target System

As the sow is served, the dates are worked out and chalked up. Where weekly batch weaning on a Thursday or Friday is practised, then a blank board on the following Friday is an early warning that something is beginning to go wrong. This early warning, or indication of problems arising, should be the basis for the day-to-day recording systems. Actions can then be taken before things have gone badly adrift. One of the best ways of doing this is by operating a target system for pigs born, reared and sold and food used. This can be done on a monthly or quarterly basis and a pattern is quickly established and comparison is then made between what is actually achieved and the target figures. Any slight deviation from this regular pattern gives an early warning of problems, and an on-the-spot investigation can be initiated immediately.

A Target system will need to be worked out for the individual farm as management systems vary. Working out targets and watching the variations and the reasons for the variations are in themselves a good discipline and can tell the stockman and manager a tremendous amount about pig performance.

Targets can be set for services and farrowings per month with a special watch on repeat services. A useful target is also provided by monitoring the gap between service and weaning. Food usage per month is another fairly simple target, especially with the breeding herd, but not so simple with the bulk food supplies in the feeding herd.

An example of a target system for a 100-sow herd with three- and five-week weaning, buying all compound feeds and buying all replacement gilts, would be as follows:

Production Guides and Targets—100-Sow Breeding Herd

	3-week weaning	5-week weaning
Farrowing index	2·45	2·2
Numbers born alive	10·8	11·0
Nos. reared per litter	9·5	9·6
Weaning weight	5·5kg	12kg
Mortality %, birth to weaning	Below 12%	Below 12%
Pigs reared, sow/year	23·0	21
Farrowings per month	20–21	18–19
Services per month	22–23	20–21
Weaners per year	2,300	2,100
Weaners per month	190	175
Boar requirements	4 or 5	4 or 5
Food per sow and gilt (including boar and creep)	1·0 tonne	1·1 tonne
Total food/year	100 tonnes	110 tonnes
Total food/month	8–9 tonnes	9–10 tonnes
Replacement gilts per year	30–35	30–35

Production Guides and Targets: Feeding Herd—100 Sows and Progeny

		3 weeks	5 weeks
Weaning at			
Live Pork wt. at slaughter	59–61kg		
Days to slaughter	120–135		
Feed conversion ratio	2·5–2·75		
		tonnes	*tonnes*
Feed per year		264–300	240–277
Feed per month		22– 25	20– 23
Cutter			
Live wt. at slaughter	75– 82kg		
Days to slaughter	143–170		
Feed conversion ratio	2·7–2·9		
Feed per year		383–458	350–418
Feed per month		32– 38	29– 35
Bacon			
Live wt. at slaughter	86– 93kg		
Days to slaughter	165–190		
Feed conversion ratio	3·0–3·25		
Feed per year		500–584	457–533
Feed per month		42– 49	38– 44
Heavy Pigs			
Live wt. at slaughter	109–120kg		
Days to slaughter	200–220		
Feed conversion ratio	3·8–4·0		
Feed per year		832–974	759–889
Feed per month		69– 81	63– 74

the newer computer systems which will forecast a whole range of figures including return on capital. However, the end result will only be as good as the records and information supplied in the first place, and this emphasises the importance of recording in pig husbandry.

Physical Production Standards and Some Efficiency Factors

As an aid to setting some realistic yardsticks and guidelines I have suggested a series of figures which are given below. Standards for physical performance figures are relatively easy to set out as they are fairly constant, but they will vary from farm to farm as the management systems differ. Targets which include the cost of food are difficult to arrive at as these change pretty quickly, but the amount of food can be accurately calculated. Some care, however, is needed with feed costs and amounts as this is obviously related to the performance of the food, so that cost per kg of lean meat produced is the most precise guide to the cost of pig-meat production on the farm.

BREEDING HERD

	Below average	Average	Good	Target
Pigs born litter	9·5	10·0	10·5	11·0
Pigs weaned litter	8·0	8·5	9·5	10·0
Litters/Sow/Year				
3-week weaning	2·0	2·2	2·35	2·45
5-week weaning	1·9	2·0	2·15	2·25
6-week weaning	1·8	1·9	2·05	2·15
Pigs/Sow/Year				
3-week weaning	16	18·7	22·32	24·5
5-week weaning	15·2	17·0	20·42	22·5
6-week weaning	14·4	16·15	19·47	21·5
Mortality before weaning	18%	15%	13%	Below 12%
Weight of Weaner, kg				
3-week weaning	4·08	4·53	4·98	5·44
5-week weaning	8·16	9·52	10·43	11·34
6-week weaning	10·43	11·34	12·70	13·60
Feed used per weaner including all creep	107·00	91·00	77·00	66·00

FEEDING HERD FCR

	Below average	Average	Good	Target
FCR				
Pork 62·0kg	2·75	2·6	2·5	2·4
Cutter 75·0kg	2·9	2·8	2·7	2·6
Bacon 89·0kg	3·3	3·15	3·0	2·9
Heavy 118·0kg	4·0	3·8	3·5	3·4
	Below average	Average	Good	Target
Days to Slaughter				
Pork	135	128	124	120
Cutter	170	156	150	143
Bacon	190	180	170	165
Heavy	220	215	208	200
Mortality	4%	2%	1·5%	1%

Food Cost per £100 Livestock Output

Livestock output =
> (Total stock sales + closing stock valuation)

minus
> (Total stock purchases + opening stock valuation)

Therefore:

$$\text{Food cost per £100 livestock output} = \frac{\text{Food cost}}{\text{Livestock output}} \times 100$$

Food cost per £100 livestock output is affected by changes in prices of inputs and outputs so that this calculation does not always precisely reflect managerial efficiency but nevertheless is a good guide for comparative purposes.

Food Cost Standards per £100 livestock output

Enterprise	Poor £	Average £	Good £
Breeding and feeding	80	75	70
Breeding and selling weaners	80	70	60
Buying weaners and feeding	85	80	75

Other Costs per £100 Livestock Output

The other principal costs involved are labour and veterinary charges.

These can be worked out on a similar basis for comparison. Labour costs will vary from £8 per £100 livestock output to a figure of £15 per £100 livestock output.

The following table from the Cambridge Pig Management Scheme (1977) summarises these major costs, highlighting the differences between the most profitable and the least profitable systems.

Costs and Margins per £100 Livestock Output
(Standard deviations in parentheses)

	Average	Most* profitable	Least* profitable
Number of Farms	146	20	20
Costs and margins per £100 output	£	£	£
Feed	68·20 (7·99)	59·26 (4·87)	83·75 (11·57)
Labour	10·46 (3·83)	7·92 (2·60)	15·42 (4·79)
Other costs	11·65 (3·69)	10·22 (2·70)	15·87 (6·94)
Total costs †	90·31 (9·29)	77·40 (3·72)	115·04 (8·27)
Margin	+9·69 (9·24)	+22·60 (3·72)	—15·04 (8·27)
	100	100	100
Valuation increase (incl. in margin)	£2·17	£4·03	—£1·07

* Selected on margins per £100 livestock output.
† No charge has been included for interest on capital.

		Average	Most* profitable	Least* profitable
Weights and prices of purchases†				
Weaners	liveweight	26kg (2·99)	25kg (1·80)	28kg (1·20)
	price per pig	£23·51 (1·56)	£23·33 (1·14)	£25·17 (1·45)
Stores	liveweight	33kg (6·54)	0	31kg (1·74)
	price per pig	£27·21 (3·43)	0	£27·22 (0·69)
Weights and prices of sales†				
Weaners	liveweight	26kg (2·16)	26kg (2·34)	27kg (1·69)
	price per pig	£23·15 (1·14)	£23·64 (1·42)	£22·93 (1·06)
Stores	liveweight	41kg (8·94)	45kg (4·76)	33kg (1·32)
	price per pig	£30·49 (5·47)	£33·12 (3·09)	£26·71 (2·07)
Porkers	deadweight	49kg (3·00)	50kg (1·80)	47kg (1·80)
	price per kg dwt	90p (2·36)	90p (2·16)	89p (1·00)
	price per pig	£43·76 (2·61)	£44·73 (1·86)	£41·32 (2·31)
Cutters	deadweight	65kg (5·94)	69kg (4·55)	62kg (4·14)
	price per kg dwt	83p (2·77)	83p (1·20)	84p (2·13)
	price per pig	£54·38 (3·58)	£57·64 (3·54)	£51·88 (2·55)
Baconers	deadweight	68kg (2·43)	71kg (1·03)	68kg (0·78)
	price per kg dwt	84p (1·26)	84p (1·45)	85p (0·85)
	price per pig	£57·36 (1·86)	£59·21 (1·65)	£57·19 (1·01)
Heavies	deadweight	92kg (1·62)	0	83kg
	price per kg dwt	76p (0·78)	0	77p
	price per pig	£69·66 (1·33)	0	£63·84
Sales percentages		%	%	%
Weaners		26·4	25·3	26·8
Stores		5·8	6·3	11·3
Porkers		17·5	26·3	23·1
Cutters		27·1	24·7	30·6
Baconers		19·1	17·3	7·0
Heavies		3·8	0	0·8
Casualties/culls		0·4	0·2	0·4
		100	100	100

* Selected on margins per £100 livestock output.
† Haulage, marketing charges and levies have been added to the cost of pigs purchased and deducted from the value of pigs sold.

NAC Pig Demonstration Area Results 1973–76

The following results tell a remarkable story of a unique pig herd over a period of five years. The unit is sponsored by RASE, MLC and BOCM Silcock. The unit was originally established in 1963 but it was in 1967, after promise of financial support from PIDA, that a five-year rebuilding programme was planned and implemented. At the same time a policy decision was taken to replace the existing herd by the adoption of a planned cross-breeding policy using a small, pure-bred grandparent herd and AI to produce planned crossbred females which were mated to tested boars to produce the slaughter generation for pork and bacon.

These results are achieved in a wide variety of buildings under demonstration conditions with a constant stream of visitors throughout the year as well as a major influx of visitors at the Royal Show each year.

NAC Results 1973-80

Breeding Herd

	1973	1974	1975	1976	1979	1980	MLC average 1980
Average number of sows and gilts in herd	145	143	152	176	196	201	160
Average number of unserved gilts	9	9	7	11	9	11	—
Average number of litters per sow and gilt*	2.3	2.5	2.4	2.4	2.44	2.53	2.2
Average number of pigs born alive per litter	10.3	10.0	10.1	10.4	10.18	10.18	10.4
Percentage mortality	11.7	10.4	10.0	10.7	9.9	11.10	12.8
Average number of pigs reared per litter	9.1	9.0	9.1	9.3	9.2	9.05	9.0
Average number of pigs reared per sow and gilt	19.9	21.3	21.8	22.4	22.44	22.85	19.8
Average weight of pigs reared (kg)	6.0	6.0	5.0	5.2	6.2	6.1	18.0
Meal equivalent per pig reared (kg)	59	56	55	52	62	51	86
Feed cost per pig reared (£)	4.20	5.09	4.35	4.91	8.50	7.17	11.6
Feed consumption per kg pig produced (kg)	9.0	10.0	10.1	10.2	9.89	8.50	4.8
Feed cost per kg pig produced (pence)	64	90	80	95	136.0	119.7	0.83
Quantity of feed per sow and gilt (tonnes)	1.17	1.17	1.14	1.05	1.200	1.051	1.7
Cost of feed per sow and gilt (£)	85.21	108.43	90.41	98.48	160.26	138.40	—
Cost per tonne meal equivalent of feed (£)	71.45	91.14	79.33	93.77	137.18	140.84	133.3

* Number adjusted for unserved gilts.

Feeding Herd

	1979	1980
Number of pigs sold	4,108	4,010
Weight of pigs sold (kg)	75	76.25
Weight of pigs brought into herd (kg)	6	6.1
Food conversion ratio	2.5	2.32
Feed cost per kg liveweight gain (p)	35.9	35.90
Cost per tonne compound food (£)	143.83	154.77
Feed cost from weaning to slaughter (£)	24.20	25.60

The breeding-herd results show a very consistent standard over the years, in many ways reflecting the picture of the national herd, with an increase in size and improved results with earlier weaning. Pigs reared per sow have increased to 22·85, whilst the quantity of food used per sow has been brought down. The steady inflation in food costs is clearly shown and the results are also compared with MLC averages for 1980.

The feeding-herd figures over the past two years ending 1979 and 1980 have been extremely good with a feeding-herd feed conversion of 2·32 for pigs slaughtered at almost 77kg.

These figures are taken from MLC feed-recording figures and indicate the high standard of feed, breed and management policies followed. Above all, they are a tribute to the dedication and efficiency of the management team and staff who are involved in the day-to-day running of the unit.

National Pig Awards

Mention should also be made of these Awards sponsored by the Cotswold Pig Development Company and the Meat and Livestock Commission.

The scheme's objectives are to identify farmers who have improved production through the use of MLC records, to gain recognition for these people's excellence in pig management and to stimulate interest in the part which record-keeping plays in efficient management.

The competition is open to all producers who are members of the MLC Pig Feed Recording Scheme and who have a minimum unit size of 50 breeding sows or 500 feeding pigs. The Awards are based on the last year's results.

There are five award categories: best overall performance, two awards for breeding herds (weaning at under 25 days and weaning at 25 days or more) and two for best feeding-herd performance (for units with both breeding and feeding herds and for units with feeding herds only).

Some outstanding results have been achieved in all categories since the scheme started in 1979, with some award-winning herds producing over 25 pigs/sow/year.

Gross and Net Margins

Tables (a) and (b) summarise calculated gross margins for different production systems. These gross margins are calculated on a monthly basis throughout the year to monitor closely the economics of pig production in the major systems.

The calculations use the physical information (feed quantities, sale weights, etc.) from the MLC Pig Feed Recording Scheme, feed costs from a sample of recorded herds, and average pig prices compiled by MLC's Economics Department.

Breeding-only and Combined Breeding and Feeding Herds

Table (a) shows the average calculated gross margins for 1980 for combined breeding and feeding herds by production system compared with 1979 and the previous five-year average. The average combined gross margins for 1980 were appreciably higher than in 1979; 18 per cent in the case of weaner production, 30 per cent for pork, 46 per cent for cutter, 29 per cent for bacon and 61 per cent for heavy pig production. These increases were generally above the level of inflation; after adjustment using the General Retail Price Index the overall average calculated gross margin across systems in 1979 was £9·88 per pig compared with £11·63 in 1980. The updated five-year averages varied from £7·20 per pig for weaner production to £14·54 per pig for bacon production. The 1980 averages were close to, or slightly above, the last five-year averages, except for weaner production, and were able to meet fixed costs and leave positive net margins.

TABLE (a). Average calculated gross margins per pig for combined breeding and feeding herds by system of production

	1975–79 average	1979	1979 adjusted for inflation* (£ per pig)	1980	1976–80 average adjusted for inflation*
Weaner production	5·30	5·54	6·54	6·52	7·20
Pork	6·70	6·63	7·82	8·62	8·88
Cutter	7·94	7·98	9·42	11·69	11·10
Bacon	10·62	11·45	13·51	14·82	14·54
Heavy	7·75	10·28	12·13	16·50	11·40

* Based on General Retail Price Index: rates 17% in 1975–76; 12% 1976–77; 8% 1977–78; 16% 1978–79; 18% 1979–80.

All systems showed a substantial improvement in gross margins in 1980, even after adjusting for inflation. The averages for 1980 were close to the adjusted five-year averages.

Feeding-only Herds

Table (b) shows the average calculated gross margins per pig for feeding-only herds by system of production for 1980 compared with 1979 and the previous five-year average.

TABLE (b). Average calculated gross margins per pig for feeding-only herds by system of production

	1975–79 average	1979	1979 adjusted for inflation* (£ per pig)	1980	1976–80 average adjusted for inflation*
Pork	1·72	0·29	0·34	1·91	1·28
Cutter	2·23	0·50	0·59	2·46	1·91
Bacon	4·63	2·39	2·82	5·74	4·56
Heavy	2·92	0·96	1·13	4·39	2·55

* Based on General Retail Price Index.

Table (c) presents average calculated net margins by system of production for 1980 and 1979. Net margins are calculated by deducting estimates of fixed costs—labour, housing and equipment depreciation—from the monthly gross margins. In these calculated net margins it is assumed that buildings are five years old and half-way through their write-off period of 10 years. The cost is an amortisation of the original building cost and the rate of interest which was charged at the time the building was erected, ie five years previously. Fixed costs and consequent net margins are very sensitive to the building charge.

TABLE (c). Average calculated net margins per pig by system of production

	1979	*1980* *(£ per pig)*	*1976–80* *average* *adjusted for* *inflation**
Weaner production	0·60	1·57	0·65
Breeding and feeding			
Pork	—1·18	1·01	—1·24
Cutter	—0·72	3·01	—0·41
Bacon	2·51	5·36	1·81
Heavy	0·55	5·05	—1·76
Feeding-only			
Bacon	—1·24	1·78	0·15
Heavy	—3·34	—0·02	—1·99

* Based on General Retail Price Index.

Calculated net margins in 1980 were appreciably above the 1979 figures and the adjusted five-year averages. All systems, except feeding only herds selling heavy pigs, produced positive net margins. However, despite the marked improvement in 1980 average net margins, the advantage was relatively modest in situations where an investment had been made in buildings in the last five years.

Source: MLC *Commercial Pig Production Yearbook 1980.*

CAPITAL REQUIREMENTS

Any discussion on pig performance will inevitably turn back to overall profitability and how this can be measured. The practical answer will often be the cash balance in the bank at the end of the year, but percentage return on capital invested will probably give a better answer. This figure is not easy to get at because many established units grow in size over an unspecified period of time and profits are ploughed back without any clear indication of the amounts involved.

Further complications occur where the unit is part of a general livestock complex on the mixed farm, as many capital items are shared amongst several enterprises. Allowances have also to be made in the case of tenant's or landlord's capital and adjustments may have to be made for the owner-occupier. Problems arise with valuation of buildings on the established pig farm, and no precise figure can be arrived at for between-farm comparisons.

Capital is usually arbitrarily divided under two headings.

Fixed Capital

This covers the cost of all housing, fixed equipment, sitework, services and the initial cost of the purchase of breeding stock.

Working Capital

This is the cash which will be required over and above fixed capital for current expenditure to keep the unit in operation. In practical terms this will be the cost of feed, labour and overheads incurred whilst the pigs are being reared and fattened.

These are the accepted definitions, but they are varied on occasions so that care must be used when making comparisons.

Fortunately the University surveys which have concentrated on existing farms have arrived at a formula for estimating capital requirements and these are highlighted in the Cambridge report.

Capital

The assessment of capital is intended to reflect the average amount required for the established herds in the scheme. Breeding stock are included at the average of the opening and closing valuations. Buildings, including those rented, are allowed for together with all equipment. Working capital is also included to cover feed, labour and other costs over the expected average time pigs remain on the farm (in established herds where farrowings are evenly spread throughout the year, the average working capital per pig will be approximately half its total cost).

Interest Charge

No charge has been included for interest on capital.

These figures show a detailed breakdown of the various types of pigmeat production classified according to slaughter weight and market outlets.

Although the sample is not very large, a consistent pattern has emerged over the years which shows that bacon production has given the best return on capital employed.

Very clearly 1979 and 1980 have both been very difficult years in all types of pig production, with 1980 showing a slight recovery. In retrospect 1976 and 1978 were comparatively profitable years, and these figures dramatically illustrate the cyclical nature of pig production.

Over this period the specialist bacon producer has generally done best, but this demands skilful management to meet carcase quality requirements, with particular emphasis on feeding levels and systems, as well as choice of genetic material and breeding programme.

Pork and cutter production are valid alternatives, but specialist production of the heavy pig, since the increase in the cost of cereals, has produced comparatively low returns on capital employed.

A Comparison of Pork, Cutter, Bacon and Heavy Pig Production*
(Breeding and Feeding)

	Pork	Cutter	Bacon	Heavy
Number of farms	25	37	27	10
Deadweight per pig	48kg	65kg	68kg	92kg
Standard deviation	(2·99)	(5·23)	(2·53)	(1·62)
Net price per kg deadweight	90p	83p	84p	76p
Standard deviation	(2·04)	(2·30)	(1·17)	(0·78)
Feeding results				
Mortality percentage	2·4%	2·0%	2·5%	1·9%
Feed conversion rate	3·00	3·26	3·31	3·71
Standard deviation	(0·41)	(0·25)	(0·31)	(0·28)
5-year average conversion rate	3·14	3·40	3·41	3·88
Cost of meal per tonne	£126·33	£118·22	£119·37	£113·84
Standard deviation	(12·92)	(8·59)	(10·11)	(3·66)
Percentage compound feed used	56%	19%	34%	2%
Feed costs per kg liveweight gain	37·9p	38·4p	39·3p	42·2p
Standard deviation	(5·27)	(3·36)	(4·16)	(2·55)
Total costs per kg liveweight gain	46·0p	46·3p	47·3p	49·0p
Standard deviation	(6·74)	(3·96)	(5·12)	(2·60)
Feeding costs per pig	£	£	£	£
Feed	18·51	26·84	28·66	41·67
Labour	1·57	2·54	2·40	3·15
Other costs	1·92	2·64	2·97	3·23
Mortality charge	·45	·36	·47	·35
Total feeding costs	22·45	32·38	34·50	48·40
Weaner cost†	18·36	18·36	18·36	18·36
Breeding and feeding costs	40·81	50·74	52·86	66·76
Net price (including bonus)	43·54	54·61	57·76	70·00
Margin (excluding interest)	2·73	3·87	4·90	3·24
Interest charge‡	7·16	8·44	8·69	9·84
Profit per pig	4·43	4·57	3·79	6·60
Margin per pig 1979	£1·26	£1·57	£2·60	£1·51
(excluding 1978	£4·45	£6·66	£6·23	£6·23
interest) 1977	—£1·15	—£0·30	£0·17	£2·42
1976	£4·81	£5·41	£6·54	£3·83
Quantity of feed per pig	kg	kg	kg	kg
Breeding per weaner	82	82	82	82
Feeding per pig	146	228	241	366
Total feed	228	310	323	448
Total feed per kg deadweight (kg)	4·73	4·73	4·75	4·89

* To qualify for inclusion in one of the four groups at least 80 per cent by value of pigs sold had to be in that category. As only 10 farms are now included in the heavy pig group certain of the averages may be less reliable.

† The weaner charge is the average production cost of farms in the scheme.

‡ Interest charged at 19 per cent on the value of breeding stock, buildings and equipment and working capital.

Capital Requirements and Returns (1977)

Capital requirements per sow	Pork £	Cutter £	Bacon £	Heavy £
Value of sow	81	81	81	81
Share of boar's value	7	7	7	7
Housing and equipment	441	515	513	543
Working capital	168	219	245	327
Total capital	697	822	846	958
	%	%	%	%
Return on capital 1980	7·2	8·7	10·7	6·3
(excluding 1979	3·8	3·7	6·1	—3·1
interest) 1978	15·3	18·0	16·3	15·3
1977	—4·1	—0·9	0·5	—6·2
1976	22·8	20·4	23·3	12·1

Notes: 1. To qualify for inclusion in one of the four groups at least 80 per cent by value of pigs sold
had to be in that category. As only 10 farms are now included in the heavy pig group certain
of the averages may be less reliable.
2. The weaner charge is the average production cost of farms in the scheme.
3. Interest charged at 19 per cent on the value of breeding stock, buildings and equipment
and working capital.

However, on a comparative basis, the variations between farms
within each group is usually greater than the difference between the
groups. This indicates that the level of efficiency achieved is probably
more important than the type of production selected. This fact is again
illustrated in that most years the 10 most profitable farms usually
include three or four bacon producers with the balance made up from
other types of production including the sales of weaners, pork, cutter
and heavy pigs.

Capital requirements are also discussed in detail in a section in the
MAFF Pig Husbandry & Management Bulletin 193 published by
HMSO.

During the past two or three years many new units have been
established as specialist enterprises on green field sites and quite clear
indications of capital requirements can be worked out. ADAS (SE
Region) have published their excellent 'Blueprint for a 200-Sow Unit
producing Pigs for Pork and Bacon'. This publication sets out the
capital costs involved in establishing a new unit of this size, with other
sections on Finance, Breeding, Housing and Management.

CAPITAL REQUIREMENTS FOR A LARGE INTENSIVE UNIT

I have been personally involved in the establishment of a number of
new units, and in this section I have set out an example of a capital
proposal for a 250-sow unit. This herd produces pigs for slaughter at
about 91kg liveweight, which at the present time would be ideal for
the bacon market but could easily switch to a mixed cutter (75kg) and
a heavier-graded pig at 100kg.

Management of the unit is based upon individual housing in stalls during pregnancy, with farrowing and rearing in partially slatted crates.

FIXED CAPITAL

Housing

	£	£	£
Sow stalls 200 × £100	20,000		
Farrowing places 50 × £450	22,500		
Flat decks 657 places × £25	16,875		
Fattening pens 1,350 places × £40	54,000		
Gilt pens and sick bay	2,000		
		115,375	
Siteworks, services and office facilities	13,000	13,000	
Machinery and equipment including feeding		12,500	
			140,875

Stock purchase			
250 Maiden gilts @ £75	18,750		
10 Boars @ £150	1,500		
		20,250	
			20,250

WORKING CAPITAL

Feed (part first year)	50,000		
Labour (75 per cent of total bill)	12,000		
Overheads (part share)	10,000		
		72,000	

SUMMARY TOTAL CAPITAL REQUIREMENTS

Housing, siteworks, services, etc.	140,875
Breeding stock	20,250
Working capital in first year	72,000
TOTAL	£233,125

Litters would then be moved at three weeks to flat-deck weaner houses and fattened in fully enclosed houses with controlled ventilation. All foods would be bought in as compounds and hybrid gilts brought in to replace the entire herd over a three- to four-year period. Performance tested boars would be used. A four-man team would be employed which would allow a good deal of free time for stockmanship.

Assumptions, Efficiency Factors and Explanatory Notes

1. Depreciation on livestock housing and fixtures is based on a 10-year life and a straight-line method of calculation. Plant and machinery is expected to have a five-year life and has been depreciated again on a straight-line method.
2. These costs will vary according to access and topography. All buildings and site works will conform with the building regulations and current legislation.

3. No allowances have been made for staff housing.
4. Interest, taxation charges and financial charges have not been included. These can be calculated for the particular project when available.

Breeding Stock

The initial pool will be 50 gilts and eight boars with 200 gilts following, delivered at two-weekly intervals and in batches of 25.
Over a four-year period the cycle of replacement will be as follows:

Year	1	2	3	4
Gilts	10	60	85	80
Boars	—	3	4	3

Labour

A four-man team is required:

	£
One manager	5,500
Head stockman	4,200
Stockman	3,500
Student	2,800
	£16,000

Feed

Compound feed (nuts or pellets delivered in bulk—list price December 1977:

	Per tonne
Breeding nuts	£95·00
Creep feed	£170·00
Grower/finisher	£111·00

Total Feed Costs

Year	1	2	3	4
	£	£	£	£
Sows and litters	20,205	26,125	26,125	26,125
Boars	950	950	950	950
Feeding pigs	42,364	143,606	143,606	143,606
	63,519	170,681	170,681	170,681

Efficiency Factors

Sows: Daily 1·8kg pregnancy.
          Daily 4·5kg lactation.
This is equivalent to 1·1 tonne per sow per year, including creep feed.

Boars: One tonne per year.

Feeding Pigs: Feed conversion rate of 3·0 from 5·4kg at weaning to 88·4kg at slaughter.

Weanders transferred to feeding herd at 5·4kg at weaning at three weeks.

Summary of Efficiency Factors

Year	1	2	3	4
Litters/sow/year	2·1	2·2	2·2	2·2
Pigs/reared/litter	8·5	9·5	9·5	9·5
Pigs/sow/year	17·8	20·9	20·9	20·9
Feed conversion ratio from 5·4kg to 88·4kg	3·0	3·0	3·0	3·0

Overheads: The figure for overheads includes repairs, maintenance, heat, light, fuel and water.

Year	1	2	3	4
	£	£	£	£
Veterinary fees and medicines	2,500	2,200	2,200	2,500
Fuel/water	3,500	3,500	3,800	3,800
Insurance	1,000	1,000	1,000	1,200
Miscellaneous/Secretarial services	3,000	3,100	3,000	3,500
	10,000	9,800	10,000	11,000

Summary of Operating Costs

Year	1	2	3	4
	£	£	£	£
Stock	19,250	4,950	6,975	6,450
Feed	63,519	170,681	170,681	170,681
Labour	12,000	16,000	16,000	16,000
Overheads	10,000	9,800	10,000	11,000
	104,769	201,431	203,756	204,131

Revenue

All earnings for the unit come from the sale of meat pigs and cull sows and boars.

Sales

Year	1	2	3	4
Nos. of meat pigs sold	1,552	5,175	5,175	5,175
Nos. of cull sows and boars	10	63	89	83
Sales value	£80,084	£269,111	£270,931	£270,511

A net price of 75p per kg deadweight is used in the calculations, with both cull sows and boars valued at £70 each.

Stock Valuation

To arrive at a more accurate revenue figure for year 1, an adjustment to stock valuation has been made so that the value of pigs produced but not yet slaughtered can be calculated. For valuation purposes weaners produced on the farm have been valued at the following figures:

0– 6 weeks	£15 per pig
6–12 weeks	£30 per pig
12–23 weeks	£45 per pig

Profitability and Return on Capital

Year	1	2	3	4
	£	£	£	£
Capital employed	233,125	233,125	233,125	233,125
Revenue	80,084	269,111	270,931	270,511
Operating costs	104,769	204,431	203,656	204,131
Stock adjustments	+28,500	—338	+411	—
Depreciation	14,000	14,000	14,000	14,000
Profit before interest and tax	—10,185	53,342	53,686	52,380
Return on capital before tax	—	22·9%	23%	22·5%

All figures are in £s and have been calculated on the basis of current values. No calculations have been made of financial charges or interest rates as these will vary according to circumstances.

Cash Flow

The cash flow indicates monthly cash requirements and provides at a glance a summary of costs and revenues. Most important of all, it shows clearly where peak capital demands occur during the critical build-up period, and a specimen cash-flow table is shown in Figure 39.

Profitability and Sensitivity to Changes in Costs and Performance Standards

The figures quoted for a 250-sow unit working very efficiently and employing almost a quarter of a million pounds are not very encouraging. This only reflects the current state of the pig industry in the UK at the end of 1977, and new investment on these terms is highly unlikely. Expansion from a small base or a change in management policy from five-week to three-week weaning would probably give a better return on capital than the new unit.

However, large units are extremely sensitive to small changes in the price of feed and the end product. The following figures, along with improved performance standards, clearly show this.

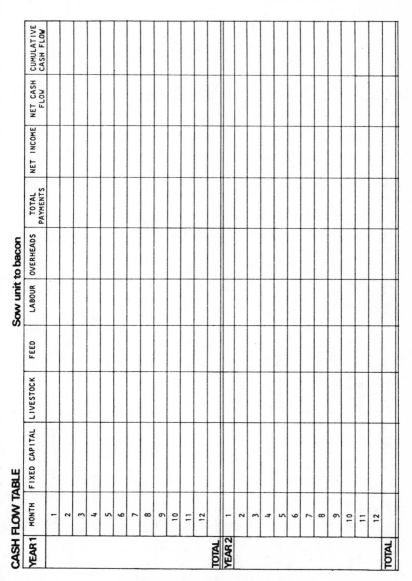

Fig. 39. *Specimen of cash flow table.*

FACTORS AFFECTING PROFITABILITY OF BREEDING PIGS

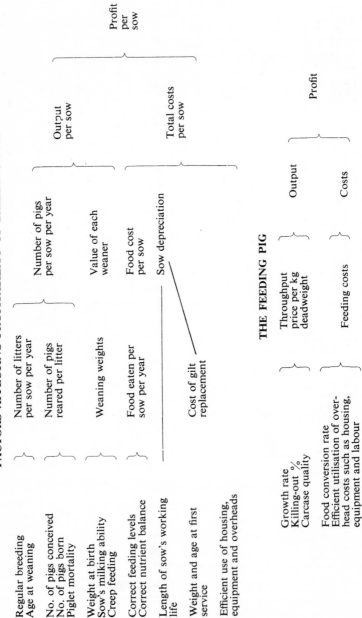

Regular breeding
Age at weaning
}
Number of litters per sow per year
}
Number of pigs per sow per year
}
Output per sow
}
Profit per sow

No. of pigs conceived
No. of pigs born
Piglet mortality
}
Number of pigs reared per litter

Weight at birth
Sow's milking ability
Creep feeding
}
Weaning weights

Value of each weaner

Correct feeding levels
Correct nutrient balance
}
Food eaten per sow per year
}
Food cost per sow
}
Total costs per sow

Length of sow's working life

Weight and age at first service
}
Cost of gilt replacement
}
Sow depreciation

Efficient use of housing, equipment and overheads

THE FEEDING PIG

Growth rate
Killing-out %
Carcase quality
}
Throughput price per kg deadweight
}
Output
}
Profit

Food conversion rate
Efficient utilisation of overhead costs such as housing, equipment and labour
}
Feeding costs
}
Costs

Sensitivity—250 sows/progeny to bacon.

Meat price. The addition of 5p per kg above 75p/kg would increase overall profitability by £16,818 per year.

Feed price. A fall in the price of feed by £5 per tonne would increase profit by £8,000 per year.

Pigs/sow/year. The addition of 1·0 pig per sow per year, from 20·9 to 21·9, would add £6,000 per year to profits.

Feed efficiency. Reduction of feed conversion rate from 3·0 to 2·8 would increase profits by £10,000 per year.

In a volatile situation, where sensitivity changes can have such a dramatic effect on profits, it would be prudent to make use of a system based on the computer 'model' pig, details of which will be found in Chapter 12.

If all the price advantages and new performance standards could be achieved, the cumulative effect would be to lift return on capital from the figure quoted of around 20 per cent to a new level of 38 per cent.

Profitability—Overall Check

Finally, two charts which neatly illustrate the factors that should be checked in monitoring the performance and profitability of the breeding and feeding herds. These can be used rather like the fault-finding charts that trace the cause of engine failure when your car fails to start! Once again, the major factor of good quantity, quality and cost is highlighted, but for almost every item there is the inevitable combination of correct choice and balance of breeding, housing, management and health factors.

Chapter 12

CURRENT DEVELOPMENTS AND A FORWARD LOOK

I WOULD like to mention some aspects of the pig industry that are currently of topical interest, and have a brief forward look at one or two areas.

POLITICAL SITUATION

The main problem area at the time of writing (the end of December 1977) is the political situation, as the final transition is made to full membership of the EEC. The British pig farmer has had a raw deal over the past 18 months because the fall in value of sterling has affected the 'Green Pound'—the unit of currency used to operate the Common Agricultural Policy. On top of this, monetary compensatory amount subsidies paid on imported bacon and canned pigmeat products have played havoc with the UK market and producers' margins. Add to this the Government wage-freeze policy and lower consumer spending and the outlook is rather depressing.

However, sterling does appear to be recovering and Government action will surely sort out some of the anomalies in MCAs during 1978. OECD forecasts predict a general recovery in the UK economy, which should lead to more money for the housewife to spend on food purchase.

The UK pig industry cannot survive without some assurances for long-term profitability. A stable background must be provided in which pig producers are encouraged to invest capital on which they will receive a reasonable return.

INFORMATION SERVICES

Until the early 1970s it was reasonably easy to forward budget for an intensive pig enterprise. This is no longer the case for a number of reasons which include the cyclical nature of pig production, exacerbated by entry into the EEC. Other main reasons include the volatile world grain market, high interest rates and the fall in the value of sterling.

In this climate financial budgeting is almost impossible and a succession of budgets will need to be worked out. This may need to be done on a monthly basis, matching production levels and targets with financial targets and predictions. Commercial firms in industry have used this form of control, and large intensive units with large amounts of capital will need to follow the same pattern.

Fortunately there is much more information available on the production and marketing of pigmeat. MLC obtain, process and make available a whole range of essential information from their central role in industry. With this information the individual producer is better able to forecast and budget, as well as compare and improve physical production. In this area there is plenty of professional advice both from within MLC, from business consultants, ADAS farm management advisers, and the agricultural specialists from the major Clearing Banks.

ENERGY AND ENVIRONMENT

The energy crisis over the past few years has forced the pig industry to look more closely at its use of energy, whether this has been in the form of better utilisation of feed or improved housing.

Fortunately fundamental basic research has been concentrating on this area, especially at the Unit of Animal Physiology at Babraham, Cambridge. It is now possible to measure and quantify the amount of extra feed that will be required by a growing pig on a daily basis if the environment falls below the lower critical temperature for that pig. This will be of enormous value to the building designer when he looks at housing and floor materials, and to the environmental engineer when he considers ventilation and heating design and equipment.

Similar specific recommendations can be made for the breeding sow housed in a sow-stall house, and temperature variations below 20°C can be quantified in the amount of extra feed that will be required to maintain body condition. These are areas of pig production that have previously only been guessed at, and the commercial implications are now being understood and applied for the first time.

GROWTH MODEL

In a similar manner, research workers have been looking at the various factors in helping to choose a feeding programme for growing pigs. In practice, decisions about feeding are taken on-farm on a historical basis from previous experience, or on a trial-and-error basis by on-farm experiment. Neither method is wholly satisfactory, and workers at Edinburgh University have developed the concept of the 'model' pig, with which responses to various situations can be predicted by means of mathematical calculations which simulate numerically what the actual responses of live pigs would have been. The approach used in Edinburgh builds up the model pig from basic physiological principles and can take into account the various environmental factors.

I can see a tremendous potential use for this model at farm level, where it can be operated and linked into the computer. This can be done with portable desk-top equipment which can be linked to the computer by use of the normal telephone service. The model will no doubt be used by nutritionists and advisers as well as the technical staff of the animal feed compounders. A whole variety of problems can be set, for which solutions can be obtained. For instance, changes in level of feeding could be looked at, as well as comparing different diets and the nutrient density of the diet. There is no doubt that this computer-model approach will be used to obtain much more accurate and precise methods of feeding growing pigs.

YOUNG BOARS FOR MEAT

Currently there is interest in producing pigmeat from young boars, where traditionally male pigs have been castrated before weaning. This turns the most efficient meat-producing type of pig into the least efficient. Research work over the past 20 years confirms that the entire male pig converts feed into lean meat more efficiently than the castrate.

Results of 12 trials carried out by UK research workers show the difference between boars and castrates as follows:

FEED CONVERSION was almost always better in boars, the difference ranging from 0·14 worse to 0·44 better.

GROWTH RATE was usually better in boars, the difference ranging from 0·04kg per day worse to 0·09kg better. Where feed is freely available, a castrate may eat sufficient to grow at the same rate as, or faster than, a boar, but in such circumstances the carcase of the castrate will be very much fatter and the feed conversion much poorer.

KILLING-OUT PERCENTAGE was generally worse in boars, the difference ranging from 2·9 per cent units worse to 0·7 per cent better.

LEAN MEAT CONTENT was always higher in the boar carcases, the difference ranging from 2·3 to 10·3 per cent units. This represented an increase of up to 20 per cent in the actual weight of lean in the carcase.

Boars convert feed more efficiently because they have a greater potential for daily lean-meat deposition. Ceasing castration would lead to an almost immediate increase in lean-meat production, greater than that achieved by performance testing and selection over a number of years.

Farm Production

The actual differences in performances between boars and castrates will depend on the circumstances of production. Taking into account the relevant experimental evidence and other appropriate information, the effects in a 200-sow herd producing baconers would be expected to be on the following lines:

Feed consumption reduced;

FCE improved by 8 per cent.

Boars have a slightly reduced killing-out percentage and therefore will have to be taken to a slightly higher weight.

Effect of FCE Difference

	Castrate	Boar
Liveweight gain	72kg (18–90)	73kg (18–91)
Feed conversion rate	3·50	3·22
Feed required	252kg	235kg
Difference		—17kg
Value of difference at £112 per tonne		£1·90 per pig
Value of difference on 1,800 male pigs		£3,420

Days to Bacon Reduced

Growth rate improved by about 7 per cent;

Effect of growth difference.

	Castrate	Boar
Liveweight gain	72kg (18–90)	73kg (18–91)
Daily gain	600g	642g
Days from 18kg	120	114
Days saved per pig		6
Number of extra pigs which could be finished		85

Other Improvements

Even on a well-organised farm castration will take up 15 to 20 minutes per litter. This time will be saved and could be better utilised. The risk of infection through castration wounds will also be reduced, which is of benefit especially in early weaning systems.

Grading for the bacon market will also be improved as boar carcases can contain up to 10 per cent more lean meat than castrates, whilst the back-fat depth is also considerably reduced.

The whole boar-meat situation is well illustrated by the following MLC trial.

Performance differences; boars v castrates 25–77kg liveweight

	Boars	Castrates
Average daily gain	712	662
Feed conversion ratio	2·44	2·71
Ultrasonic measurement:		
Shoulder fat (mm)	35	38
P_1 fat (mm)	14	17
P_3 fat (mm)	14	18
Loin fat (mm)	17	21
Grade	%	%
1st	94	45
2nd	6	29
3rd	—	19
4th	—	7
	100	100

Results show that boars raised from 25 to 77kg liveweight took an average of 5·5 days less than castrates to reach slaughter weight.

Their feed-conversion ratio was 0·27 better—they ate 14kg less feed. At March 1977 prices this gave a cash saving of about £2.

Lower fat depths also brought improved grading. The 58kg boar carcases were each worth on average an extra 68p. Boars and castrates in the trial were graded according to a large buyer's cutter contract and more than 90 per cent of boars made the top grade. Only 45 per cent of castrate carcases were in this grade.

Marketing the meat is now less of a problem with boars slaughtered at a younger age than formerly. Most of the fears expressed over taint and odour by wholesale and retail meat traders have proved to be unfounded. Scientific work and surveys have been carried out in the field by the Meat Research Institute at Langford, Bristol. For the retailer, boars provide leaner carcases giving a higher percentage of saleable meat with bigger muscles making more attractive joints.

Large-scale consumer tests on boar meat were favourable, whilst adverse reaction was negligible. Boar meat has a great deal to offer to producer, processor, retailer and consumer. Close co-operation is essential to make sure that the benefits of this technique in production are realised and utilised for the various parties involved.

MLC and MAFF have given their support for production of young boars for meat, and the net benefits to producers could be worth up to £10 million pounds per year. Provided producers first ensure their market outlet, there should be a potential growth area for increased sales of fresh meat.

A FORWARD LOOK

Finally a forward look, which must be entirely speculative as rapid changes have taken place in the industry and more are likely in the next two or three years—which is as far forward as I would like to think at the present time.

Specialisation will no doubt continue, but the cyclical changes of the last two or three years have emphasised the value of the pig enterprise within the mixed farm. This family farm can often supply the management and supervisory skills that are difficult to obtain on the very large unit.

Integration with the dairy herd, where slurry is utilised for grassland and milk production, can also answer some of our pollution problems.

Fresh meat still appears to be the main growth area for UK pig production, with a reduction in the quality bacon market. With increasing fixed costs it is inevitable that the average slaughter weight of pigs must increase. It seems that the lightweight porker of about 50–60kg cannot survive, and it will be much more economical to produce and process a heavier pig of the cutter type, perhaps in the 70–80kg range, and this makes more sense all round.

There is a small but increasing export market for British pigmeat, mainly to EEC countries, of which West Germany, France and Italy are the main importers. Although the market is comparatively small, it does offer an extra outlet for the very efficient British pigmeat industry.

Basic research is needed in the field of animal behaviour, especially as we intensify production systems and knowledge in this area is very scant. At the same time more attention must be paid to animal welfare and animal comfort in the broadest sense.

It will be interesting to watch the cumulative results of CPE as they quickly build up over the next few years. The comparative performance figures between the various companies are of interest, but it is essential that the information and details of carcase dissection such as lean tissue growth rates are recognised and passed on to the commercial pig producer. Emphasis on food economy in terms of lean tissue growth will be even greater, and with improved environment there is still room for even more efficient production. Management has also a key role to play, with greater precision in feeding methods and feed distribution.

Finally, the staff. They need better working conditions, improved status and better financial rewards. How we are going to achieve this at a time of national wage restraint is another matter. Stockmen and managers generally started well behind when the pay freeze began and we must find other ways of giving them their due rewards. At the end of the day the whole industry depends upon the vital link in pig production—the man who looks after the pigs. His skill, devotion and stockmanship provide that essential ingredient that makes all the difference between profit and loss.

H

Appendix 1

ADDITIONAL READING

Chapter 2. Market Outlook
Pigs and Pig Meat, UK Farming and the Common Market. Published by National Economic Development Office.

Annual Review of Agriculture 1981.

Meat and Livestock Commission, PO Box 44, Queensway House, Bletchley, Milton Keynes MK2 2EF:
    (a) Pig Improvement Service—Feed Recording Results 1976, Report No. 3 and Report No. 4, 1977.
    (b) Economic Information Service.
        Meat Demand and Price Forecasting—Proceedings of a Symposium, April 1977.
        Monthly Market Survey—Meat and Livestock Statistics.
        UK Trade in Livestock and Meat, April 1977.
        Pig Meat—Increasing the Trade Share.
        'Constraints on Pig Meat Consumption'—G. Harrington, Proceedings of FW/MLC Conference, Bristol, February 1977.
        UK Slaughterings, Meat Production and Supplies, August 1977 and subsequent publications.
        MLC Commercial Pig Production Year Book, 1979 and 1980.
        MLC EEC Statistics, 1979.

Chapter 3. Basic Policy Decisions
'Cross-breeding and Litter Production in British Pigs', by C. Smith and J. W. B. King, Animal Production, Vol 6, part 3, pp. 265–271. October 1964.

'Farm Animals—Their Growth, Breeding and Inheritance', 3rd Edition, by J. Hammond. Published by Edward Arnold (Publishers) Ltd., 25 Hill Street, London W1X 8LL.

'Pig Production', edited by D. J. A. Cole. Proceedings of the 18th Easter School in Agricultural Science, University of Nottingham, 1971. Published by Butterworth & Co. (Publishers) Ltd., Borough Green, Sevenoaks, Kent TN15 6AB. Section 1, Genetics. Section 4, The Breeding Pig.

Meat and Livestock Commission:
    Pig Improvement Scheme Year Book 1976–77.
    Report of the Commercial Pig Study Group 1970.
    Report of the Scientific Pig Study Group 1970.

MLC Pig Improvement Services:
    Commercial Product Evaluation 1977.

MLC Report of the Pig Testing Working Party, June 1977.

Finance for Farmers and Growers 1977–78, Barclays Bank.

The Agricultural Common Market—Beyond Transition, Barclays Bank.

MLC Commercial Pig Evaluation: Annual Report, 1978–81.

Chapter 4. Housing—Basic Requirements
'The Climatic Physiology of the Pig', by L. E. Mount. Published by Edward Arnold (Publishers) Ltd.

'Pig Housing', by D. Sainsbury, MRCVS, PhD. Published by Farming Press Ltd., Wharfedale Road, Ipswich IP1 4LG.

'Controlled Enviroment', Farm Electric Handbook No. 10 (1971). Published by the Electricity Council, Trafalgar Buildings, 1 Charing Cross, London SW1A 2DS.

'Farm Wastes, Proceedings and Symposium'. Published by The Institute of Water Pollution Control, Newcastle upon Tyne University, 1970.

Farm Buildings—Cost Guide, Scottish Farm Buildings Investigation Unit, 1981.

Farm Waste Management:
General Information STL 67.
Advice on Avoiding Pollution STL 185.

Profitable Utilisation of Livestock Manures STL 161. Published by MAFF, Tolcarne Drive, Pinner, Middlesex.

How Much for a 200-Sow Unit? Power Farming, April/May 1977.

Farm Wastes Handbook. A. M. Robertson, Scottish Farm Buildings Investigation Unit.

Intensive Livestock Units—Subject Plan. Humberside County Council, July 1977.

'Pig Housing—the last ten years', Baxter and Robertson, 'Pig News and Information', 1980, Vol. 1, No. 1.

Chapter 5. Housing/Stock

'Housing the Pig', Ministry of Agriculture, Fisheries and Food Bulletin 160, 3rd Edition 1979.

'Housing the Sow and Litter', Ministry of Agriculture, Fisheries and Food Leaflet No. 51.

Farm Buildings Pocket Book, Ministry of Agriculture, Fisheries and Food Metric Edition 1971.

Pig Housing Manual, published by Farm Buildings Centre, NAC.

'Farm Building Progress', published quarterly by Scottish Farm Building Investigation Unit, Craibstone, Bucksburn, Aberdeen.

Pig Finishing Houses, MAFF Leaflet 46.

'Animal Wastes', Taiganides, Applied Science Publishers.

'Pig News and Information', quarterly by CAB.

Chapter 6. Feeding

'The Nutrient Requirements of Farm Livestock, No. 3, Pigs, Technical Reviews and Summaries,' Agricultural Research Council, 1967 HMSO.

'The Nutrient Requirements of Farm Livestock, No. 3, Pigs, Summaries of Estimated Requirements.' Agricultural Research Council, 1966 HMSO.

'Nutrient Requirements of Swine, No. 2', Sixth revised edition, 1968. Published by National Academy of Sciences, 2101 Constitution Avenue, Washington DC 20418.

'Pig Production.' Edited by D. J.A. Cole. Butterworths.
Section 3. The Growing Pig.
Section 4. The Breeding Pig.

'Applied Animal Nutrition', by E. W. Crampton and L. E. Harris. Published by W. H. Freeman & Co., 660 Market Street, San Francisco, California 94104.

'Animal Nutrition, 1969', by P. McDonald, R. A. Edwards and J. F. D. Greenhalgh. Published by Oliver & Boyd, Tweedsdale Court, Edinburgh.

'Feed Preparation', Farmelectric Handbook No. 14. Published by The Electricity Council.

Farm Mechanisation Study, No. 22, Pipeline Feeding Systems for Pigs.

March 1972. Ministry of Agriculture, Fisheries and Food.
'Practical Pig Nutrition', C. T. Whittemore and F. W. H. Elsley, Farming Press.
Do You Know? 1977 Facts and Figures about the UK Compound Animal Feedstuffs Industry. U.K.A.ST.A., 3 Whitehall Court, London SW1A 2EQ.
'Swine Production in Temperate and Tropical Environments', by W. G. Pond and J. H. Maner.
'Pig Production in the Tropics', Deverdra and Fuller, OUP.

Chapter 7. Management/Stock

'Pig Husbandry and Management', Ministry of Agriculture, Fisheries and Food Bulletin 193. HMSO.
'Blueprint for 200-Sow Unit. Progeny to Pork and Bacon.' Ministry of Agriculture, Fisheries and Food.
Model Pig Systems of the East Riding:
1. Breeding and Fattening.
2. Weaner Production.
3. Bacon Production from Purchased Weaners. ADAS.
Proceedings of the British Society of Animal Production 1972. Symposium: Artificial Rearing of Pigs. Published by Longman Group Ltd., 33 Montgomery Street, Edinburgh EH7 5JX.
Codes of Recommendations for the Welfare of Livestock. Code No. 2 Pigs. Ministry of Agriculture, Fisheries and Food.
Weaning of Pigs at 3 Weeks of Age—MAFF/ADAS.
Pigs—Service Management 1977—MAFF.
The Influence of Age of Weaning on Sow Productivity—STL 60, MAFF.
Towards More Profitable Weaner Production, STL 124, MAFF.
'The Sow—Improving Her Efficiency.' P. English, W. Smith and A. MacLean. Farming Press.
MLC Sow Management—Leaflet.
'Reproductive Failure in the Pig. Diagnosis and Control.' A. E. Wrathall. Veterinary Record, 19th March 1977.
Reproductive Disorders in Pigs. A. E. Wrathall, Commonwealth Agricultural Bureaux, Farnham Royal, Slough.
'Reproduction in the Pig', P. Hughes and M. Varley. Butterworths.

Chapter 8. Management/Staff

Pig Production Training Handbook, by Agricultural, Horticultural and Forestry Industry Training Board, Bourne House, 32–34 Beckenham Road, Beckenham, Kent BR3 4PB.
1. A Guide to the Rent Act (Agriculture) 1976. Moira Constable, Arthur Rank Centre.
2. Opportunities for Home Ownership by Agricultural Workers. Arthur Rank Centre, NAC, Kenilworth, Warwickshire.

Chapter 9. Health

'Changes in Pig Production in Britain and their Effect on the Veterinary Profession', by T. J. Alexander, from the Veterinary Record, 6th February 1971.
'Management and Disease of Pigs.' Royal Veterinary College and British Council Course. Proceedings of British Council Course. September 1971.
'Recording in Commercial Pig Units', by R. O. Weaver. The Veterinary Record, 17th July 1971.
'Pig Farmer's Veterinary Book', N. Barron. Farming Press.

TV Vet Book for Pig Farmers, TV Vet. Farming Press.

The Pig Journal—Proceedings of the Pig Veterinary Society, Volume 1 and subsequent volumes.

'Pig Diseases', D. J. Taylor. Burlington Press, Cambridge.

'Diseases of Swine', 4th Edition, H. W. Dunne and A. D. Leman. Iowa State University Press.

'Pig Health and Production Recording' Booklet 2075. MAFF Central Veterinary Laboratory, Weybridge.

Chapter 10. Recording and Management Control

'Results of Pig Management Scheme' 1977, by R. F. Ridgeon, Agricultural Economics Unit, Department of Land Economy, University of Cambridge.

'Pig Production, Yesterday, Today and Tomorrow.' University of Exeter. Agricultural Economics Unit 1980.

NAC Pig Report 1978–1980.

MLC Pig Improvement Services:
Monthly Pig Producers' Gross Margins.
Breeding and Feeding Herd Recording Averages.

MLC Pig Meat Quality—Technical Bulletin No. 19.

GENERAL

'Pigs, Their Breeding, Feeding and Management', by V. C. Fishwick. Published by Crosby, Lockwood & Son Ltd., PO Box 9, 29 Frogmore, St. Albans, Herts.

'The Production and Marketing of Pigs', by H. R. Davidson. Pubilshed by Longman Group Ltd., Longman House, Burnt Mill, Harlow, Essex CM20 2JE.

'Profitable Pig Farming', by Geoffrey Johnson. Farming Press.

Index of Research, by Meat and Livestock Commission 1976.

'Pig Management and Production', by Derek H. Goodwin. Published by Hutchinson Educational Ltd., 3 Fitzroy Square, London W1P 6JD.

'Farming Finance', by P. Clery. Farming Press.

'Pig Production—The Scientific and Practical Principles', by C. T. Whittemore. Longman.

'A.R.C. Index of Current Research on Pigs', annual publication.

'Aspects of Swine Ecology', by D. Hollier, B.O.P., Spring Green, WI.

METRIC CONVERSION TABLE

Conversion to Metric Units	Conversion from Metric Units

LINEAR MEASURE (LENGTH)

To convert	Multiply by	To convert	Multiply by
inches to millimetres	25·4	millimetres to inches	0·039
inches to centimetres	2·54	centimetres to inches	0·394
feet to metres	0·305	metres to feet	3·281
yards to metres	0·914	metres to yards	1·094
miles to kilometres	1·609	kilometres to miles	0·621

SQUARE MEASURE (AREA)

To convert	Multiply by	To convert	Multiply by
sq. inches to sq. centimetres	6·452	sq. centimetres to sq. inches	0·155
sq. feet to sq. metres	0·093	sq. metres to sq. feet	10·764
sq. yards to sq. metres	0·836	sq. metres to sq. yards	1·196
acres to hectares	0·405	hectares to acres	2·471

CUBIC MEASURE (VOLUME)

To convert	Multiply by	To convert	Multiply by
cu. inches to cu. centimetres	16·387	cu. centimetres to cu. inches	0·061
cu. feet to cu. metres	0·028	cu. metres to cu. feet	35·315
cu. yards to cu. metres	0·765	cu. metres to cu. yards	1·308

LIQUID MEASURE (CAPACITY)

To convert	Multiply by	To convert	Multiply by
fluid ounces to litres	0·03	litres to fluid ounces	33·814
quarts to litres	0·946	litres to quarts	1·057
gallons to litres	3·785	litres to gallons	0·264
imperial gallons to litres	4·546	litres to imperial gallons	0·220

WEIGHTS (MASS)

To convert	Multiply by	To convert	Multiply by
ounces avoirdupois to grams	28·35	grams to ounces avoirdupois	0·035
pounds avoirdupois to kilograms	0·454	kilograms to pounds avoirdupois	2·205
tons to metric tons	0·907	metric tons to tons	1·102

TEMPERATURE

Fahrenheit thermometer	Celsius (or Centigrade) thermometer	
32°F	freezing point of water	0°C
212°F	boiling point of water	100°C
98·6°F	body temperature	37°C

To find degrees Celsius, subtract 32 from degrees Fahrenheit and divide by 1·8.
To find degrees Fahrenheit, multiply degrees Celsius by 1·8 and add 32.

INDEX

NOTES

NOTES